IT HAD TO BE MAGIC

A DOG WORTH FIGHTING FOR

AMY AHRENSDORF

ISBN: 978-1-7358623-0-9

This book is dedicated to Laurie Brooks
Teacher, Editor and Friend

CONTENTS

1

MID-LAB CRISIS

I had two passions when I was young: canines and cooking. My dad filmed me at the age of three attempting to pick up our dachshund, whose torso was longer than my entire body. Growing up, my family owned dogs for as long as I can remember. Our pooches were part of our loving family, so I vowed to have one of my own. Little did I know then that a dog could have such an incredible impact on me, and how a canine would change my life. I certainly didn't think the magic would come from a rescue.

I met my husband, Michael, through mutual friends. It didn't take long to discover we shared a love for family, adventure, food, and canines. Michael often spoke of the dog he grew up with named Peppy, the toy poodle that didn't shed. He was the perfect breed for his family, all sufferers from horrendous allergies.

After a whirlwind eight-month romance, he proposed. A year later we married and settled into our new lifestyle and routine. But between careers, travel, and Michael's allergies, the subject of owning a dog wasn't discussed. Three short years later, we had our two boys, Charlie and Seth, born sixteen months apart. We couldn't imagine adding a puppy to the chaotic household of two energetic boys running amuck, especially after the boys' allergy tests at ages four and five revealed a severe reaction to cat hair and a moderate one to dog dander, grasses, and pollen. Our pediatrician cautioned us that the boys' health would be compromised if we brought a dog into the household.

In the midst of trying to juggle my full-time job and family responsibilities, I decided I wanted the flexibility to own a part-time business so I could spend more time with the kids. But that idea posed a challenge. If I left my corporate job, I would have to make a career change. How would I re-invent myself? And then it came to me. I could pursue my love for the culinary arts.

I had taken an interest in learning how to cook at the age of five, and by eight, earned the title of sous chef from my classically French trained mother who had taken classes from renowned chefs. She had an herb garden in the mid-sixties and often sent me out to snip the aromatics for her dishes. It wasn't an easy assignment, considering she had twenty different plants to identify. I remember inhaling the sweet smell of basil and the woody aroma of rosemary as I dashed back to the kitchen. I spent hours reading recipes and experimenting with different ingredients, hoping to wow everyone with my innate foodie gene.

Those memories were the impetus to turn my cooking hobby into a professional career. I enrolled in culinary school and attended classes at night so Michael could take care of the kids. Days after graduation, I launched my personal chef business.

Even though my part-time job afforded me more time at home, I still kept up my mantra of, "No dog," every time Charlie and Seth begged me to reconsider. I desperately wanted one as much as everyone else in the family but found their continuing allergy justification to be my redeeming argument. However, the truth of the matter was the youngsters coupled with my job were all I could handle. The first five years of their lives is still a blur in my mind, but like most parents, I survived the sleep-deprived nights and action-packed days.

The pleading continued. Every Christmas the boys held out hope there would be some sign like a dog bed or chew toy wedged behind the branches of the tree.

One afternoon in January, when the boys were in their early teens, I discovered a large shopping bag sitting on the dining room table. On the outside, a printed sign said, *for Mom*. I peered inside and giggled. A stuffed yellow Labrador Retriever puppy filled up the entire bag. I slipped my new-found buddy under my arm and walked toward the boys' bedrooms.

"Hey guys," I said in a sing-song voice. "Do you know anything about a bag that was left on the table for me? It's not my birthday and we just celebrated Christmas. I can't imagine why someone would have left me this gift."

Both kids appeared at the doorway to their rooms sporting wide smiles.

"Oh, you found it," Charlie said casually.

"Do you like her?" asked Seth.

"Very cute, guys. Is this a not-so-subtle hint?"

Seth continued, "Since you won't buy us a real dog, we thought a stuffed one would be the next best thing, you know, to remind you of how much we all want a dog. By the way, we named her Madeline."

I pulled the toy puppy with golden glass eyes and a brown nose from under my arm and held her in front of my face. "Well, hello, Madeline. You're adorable," I crooned, pulling her close to my chest. "You're the perfect addition to our family." I looked at the boys. "Are you two trying to work me?"

Charlie and Seth grinned. I tucked the huggable animal into the crook of my arm. "Maybe you should take turns keeping Madeline in your rooms. Good news is, you don't have to walk her or pick up poop." Both laughed. "Back to your homework. Dinner's at six-thir-ty——chicken and black bean enchiladas are on the menu."

Walking to the kitchen, I lifted the adorable puppy to my cheek, closed my eyes and thought for a brief second how much I wished Madeline was real.

By the time the boys were in their mid-teens, they had outgrown most allergies but not the argument for wanting a dog.

In high school, Charlie and Seth didn't need much supervision. They were growing up fast with friends of their own and activities that kept them busy when they weren't studying. With the boys needing me less and less, I was thankful to have a fulfilling job as a chef at a nearby appliance distributing company. The spacious show-room featured vignettes of luxury brand kitchen appliances plus a live galley kitchen for food preparation. I taught cooking classes, conducted product demonstrations for customers and hosted special food events. I could hardly wait to step into the culinary arena every day.

One morning, while printing out recipes in the back office, a plump, fawn-colored puppy trotted by wagging his tail. I did a double take. Who was his owner and why was he swaggering over to meet me? I stared, dropping the recipes on the tile floor. As I bent to pick them up, he plopped down on my shoes. I reached down, scooped him up into my arms and felt his warm fur. He almost wiggled out of my arms until settling down to munch on my fingers. As the smell of puppy breath washed over me, I felt a pinch on my finger. Ouch! I had forgotten baby teeth are so razor sharp. Loving every lick and flick of his wet nose that grazed my hand, I felt a twinge of yearning. He threw his head around and with large paws, pushing against my chest, he twisted from side to side. I could barely hold on to him. His atten-tion span only lasted a second, but his soft eyes gleamed at me when I rolled him on his back and scratched his tummy. I couldn't stand the thought of putting him down, but I had a bunch of people coming for lunch. *Put the puppy down, Lauren, and get back to work.*

As I lowered him to the floor, he let out a few high-pitched yips. The sound reminded me of a baby cooing. How could I resist? I lifted him back into my arms, put my face into his tummy, and breathed in his sweet smell. I decided food prep could wait. I needed to know more about the puppy snuggled in my arms.

Before I had time to look for answers, Brad, our brawny ware-house manager, popped around the corner asking if anyone had seen his Labrador Retriever, Tank. A huge smile came over my face as I reluctantly placed Tank into his open arms. The brown-eyed pup shot me a look of longing.

"Oh my gosh, Tank is adorable. Where did you find him?"

"I saw an ad in the paper that there were lab puppies for sale right down the road. I went over yesterday, met Randy, the breeder, and this is who came home with me." He glanced at Tank. "There's a bunch more looking for a good home."

"Thanks, but we aren't in the market for a dog."

"Are you sure about that? You seem to be pretty interested. If I didn't know any better, I'd say you've already caved."

"Mmmm, maybe I'll take his number just so I have it."

I jotted the breeder's number down on the back of the chocolate soufflé recipe I planned on serving that afternoon. I watched Brad slip Tank under his arm and head back to the warehouse. As the puppy's wagging tail slapped his new owner's back, I felt like a piece of my heart was going along with him. I picked up the rest of the recipes still strewn across the floor and returned to the kitchen. But as I washed my hands and tried to focus on preparing pistachio encrusted pork tenderloin with a coconut reduction sauce, steamed French green beans with shallots and thyme, black rice, and a decadent chocolate soufflé, the image of puppies just down the road distracted me. Lunch for the home builders was scheduled to be served at noon. If I didn't want to make excuses for late food service, I needed to summon some serious discipline. I sighed wistfully. *Lauren, forget about that adorable furball and get moving.*

I turned my attention to the lengthy prep list and started chopping. I ground the pistachios in the food processor, then made the sauce, reducing the coconut milk to a thick cream and adding plum sauce, Japanese mirin, chicken stock, freshly squeezed orange juice, lime leaves, and oyster sauce. Next, I whipped up the chocolate soufflé and gently scooped the velvety mixture into sugar-rimmed ramekins. By eleven o'clock the green beans were washed, shallots and thyme sautéed in olive oil, and the rice was in the steamer.

Lunch went off without a hitch. The clinking of spoons in the empty ramekins signaled I could start the clean-up. Glancing at my watch, I saw it was two-thirty. As soon as the attendees cleared the room, I moved through the showroom kitchen at light speed, scooping up serving platters and organizing left-over food into storage containers. By four o'clock, dishwashers were running and appliances were shined. I hung up my apron and returned to my desk with the prep file, looking up the number for the breeder, Randy, on the back of the soufflé recipe. I rifled through the recipes, digging to find the number. I had to see the puppies, now. I had waited all day to get my hands on one of those cutie-pies. When Randy answered, yips and whimpers echoed in the background.

"Hi, Randy, this is Lauren. I know you have some lab puppies for sale because my work colleague, Brad, brought one of them into the office today. Could I stop by and take a look?"

"If you like, you can come by right now. I have two litters," he said.

"Two litters, really? Oh my gosh. I'm just coming by to take a look. I'm not ready to buy one."

"No problem. We're not going anywhere with this lot."

A long winding gravel road ended at a white stucco farmhouse. I walked up the porch steps and saw a poster board sign saying *Pups for Sale* and an arrow pointing around the side of the house to a large backyard. Joyful yips and high-pitched squeals met my ears from the two wire kennels nestled in the grassy yard. Randy, a middle-aged man, extended his hand to introduce himself. He asked me what sex and color I had in mind.

Even though I was sure I wasn't taking a dog, I had always dreamed of owning a loving, companion-seeking lab. "Ohh, I think a female, probably yellow." What was I talking about? No, I was only there to see the puppies, not take one home.

Randy's eyes twinkled as he opened the two kennel doors. The mass of multi-colored puppies spilled out and piled up like a twenty-car collision. There were blondes, chocolates, and blacks, each one stumbling around, roughhousing with their brothers and sisters, chewing on anything in their pathway. The pups were yelping, nipping, and scattering in all directions, and I was overwhelmed with their cuteness.

As soon as I picked one up, another one would stumble toward me and munch on one of my shoes. Being surrounded by sixteen playful puppies was, in a chef's description, delicious. The situation reminded me of having sixteen of my favorite desserts and no willpower to restrain from devouring every single one. If saying no to a chocolate cake with layers of silky mousse with a ganache icing was challenging, then saying no to a dessert case with multiple choices of flavored cheesecakes, petit fours, and chewy brownies was impossible.

I couldn't resist the urge to hold the puppies in my arms, pull them in close and snuggle my face against their smooth fur. The feeling was like holding a newborn baby in a warm blanket. I felt loved. I laid down in the grass, and waited for the clumsy pooches to claim me as their jungle gym. I couldn't stop the euphoria. I could feel every ounce of restraint oozing from my fingertips as I scratched pink bellies. How did my life suddenly become so idyllic? All the arguments about why we shouldn't own a dog faded. I looked at my watch. Six-thirty! I stood brushing off dog hair, and scanned the fluffballs one last time. Feeling the pressure to get home and make dinner before the boys ate everything in the house, I turned to Randy. "I'd like to bring the family here tomorrow to see the puppies. Would six o'clock be a good time?"

"That works, but you're not coming by to buy one, right?"

We both laughed. "See you tomorrow," I said, heading toward the car. Oh, how I wanted to spend more time with the pups. I wanted, no, I needed one. Their warm coats, button noses, and little yips had overloaded my senses and infiltrated my thoughts. I envisioned a dog greeting me at the front door every evening, wagging his tail, comforting me when I cried during a sappy movie, and snuggling at night by the fireplace. Huh? We built a fire once a year living in Phoenix. Wow, I needed a reality check. The thought of bringing one home was as impractical as the two fireplaces we had in the house. After all, we lived in the desert.

The hard facts were impossible to dismiss. With Michael working full-time and me working part-time, we wouldn't have time to spend with a dog. The kid's allergies were still a concern and I questioned whether the boys would be responsible enough to initiate an exercise program. And the training. Who would take charge of that project? Would we have to hire someone and pay thousands of dollars to make sure our puppy learned basic commands like, sit, stay, down, and come? Oh, and I couldn't overlook the cost of vet care and premium food.

The arguments were like eggs hitting a Teflon saucepan: nothing stuck. I had a solution for every problem. If Brad, our warehouse manager, brought Tank to work every day, I'd ask him if he could watch my pup, too. The kids could take allergy medication and be forced to sign a binding contract that would commit them to exercising the dog on a daily basis. Done. Well, there was the training, and the other expenses, but we could add a designated dog expense line item to our monthly budget. What could it cost? Fifty dollars?

Despite the fact that I seemingly had all the answers to why we should bring a puppy into the family, there was an uneasiness bubbling up in my chest. If I was truthful in my reasoning for wanting a dog, I'd have to admit there were times when I felt detached from our family. The kids were growing up and Michael's job was requiring more out-of-town travel and long work days, including weekends. I secretly wondered if a puppy would fill the emotional void in my relationships with my husband and children.

Lauren, stop with the crazy thoughts. I'm getting caught up in the moment. I know my family loves me. I mean, deep down I think they do. Of course they do! So, what's the problem? I pulled the car off to the side of the road, unable to focus on what was in front of me. My sadness was clouding rational thinking. *Lauren, push those emotions to the curb. They're not helpful.* For a minute, I closed my eyes and remembered how it felt to hold one of the puppies.

Feeling a little better, a new conversation emerged. *The fact is, I'm a mom. And moms universally have an innate need to nurture and love. So, if the relationships have changed and I don't feel they need my care anymore, no wonder I'm feeling a void.* I was obviously having a difficult time accepting that concept. *Am I wrong to want to recapture those feelings again?* I was starting to understand why interacting with the puppies had triggered a flood of emotions. The reality was painstakingly clear. At home, I felt unappreciated. I wasn't convinced anyone needed me anymore. With all the attention the puppies had showered on me, I felt loved and wanted. Is that what happens when teens exercise their new-found independence and their mom spends a couple hours interacting with sixteen adorable fluffballs? I guess so.

I stared out the windshield daydreaming of the new adventures and love that would come my way with a puppy in my life. There was no doubt in my mind why Tank had wandered by my cubicle at work. I was going through a vulnerable time in my life, but fate had intervened. After texting the boys that dinner would be on the table by seven-fifteen, I put the car in drive and headed home.

The dinner prep of cleaning broccoli, scrubbing sweet potatoes, and preparing the chicken thighs for the grill seemed easy after the three-course luncheon at the showroom. I was pulling out a jar of dry rub from the pantry when Michael walked in the kitchen. I followed him into the bedroom, closing the door.

"Hi, hon. Hope you had a good day at work."

"Yeah, great," he said, retreating to the closet to change clothes.

"Mmmmm, there's something I want to talk to you about before we discuss it with the kids."

"What's up?" he asked, joining me in the bedroom.

"I know you're not going to believe this, but I think we should get a dog."

"What?" Michael shot me a look in disbelief. "Wait a minute. What happened to all the reasons why we've said we shouldn't have a dog?"

I walked over to Michael and placed my hand on his shoulder. "Look, I think if there was ever the right time, it's now. I want the dog to have a chance to bond with Seth before he leaves for college."

"Okay, spill," Michael said as he backed away. "Something must have happened today to make you change your mind."

I filled him in on what took place in the showroom and my visit to the breeder, not saying anything about my emotional epiphany.

"You know the kids are going to be ecstatic. I hope we're doing the right thing," Michael said hesitantly.

"Oh honey, think of it as an adventure," I said, winking.

I called everyone to the kitchen. "Before we eat, I have an announcement," I said, trying to suppress my excitement. "I know this is coming as a complete shock, but I think we should get a puppy."

Charlie and Seth were so stunned they were quiet for ten seconds, the whole time searching my eyes to see whether I was joking.

"What are you talking about?" Charlie said. "You've told us for years that we'd never get a dog. Why now?"

"Well, let's just say I had a puppy encounter at work today. You guys know Brad, our warehouse manager. He brought his lab pup into the office today——that's when I knew we should get one, too. I know, I know, I said no dog, but ..." Before I could finish my sentence, Seth left out a yell.

"Yes, yes! We are finally getting a dog!" Seth said, slapping Charlie a high five.

"So, I guess that means everyone's on board to see the puppies tomorrow?"

We made a snap decision that night. We had no idea what we were getting ourselves into when Maddie came to live with us the next day.

2

DRAMA QUEEN

The whole family agreed Maddie was the pick of the litter at eight weeks old with her creamy white coat, brown eyes, and ink-black nose. She was, in one word, adorable. Her pudgy tummy swayed from side to side as she pranced around the kitchen. Mischievous and chock full of boundless energy, she needed constant supervision, training, and exercise. Everyone helped with puppy chores on the evenings and weekends but when Michael and I were working and the kids were at school, we needed someone else to manage her. I was thrilled when Brad offered to watch her at my workplace. For the next four months, she and her sibling, Tank, kept each other company running around the warehouse. They roughhoused for hours, playing hide and seek between the boxes of refrigerators, ranges, hoods, dishwashers, and microwaves. But she outgrew her welcome when she peed on the floor, chewed up packing peanuts, and shredded cardboard. Out of dog-sitting options, I made the decision to leave Maddie at home in our fenced-in backyard. She loved swimming in the pool and roaming around on the grass. She often camped out under the misters we had installed along the roof line and enjoyed drinking cold water out of an open cooler filled with an ice block.

Although she seemed to be content outdoors, I often wondered how she amused herself for six hours a day.

Maddie could hardly wait for the boys to come home from school. The two favorite games she liked to play with Charlie and Seth were pool tag and keep-away in the back yard with their soccer ball. Seth fussed over her, giving her endless belly rubs, and Charlie spoiled her with lots of treats. She often bunked in with the boys if their doors were open at night. Maddie had a special relationship with Michael, too. They bonded during their morning walks around the neighborhood. She knew the routine so well that if Michael didn't take her out for her "constitutional," she sulked for hours.

But by the time Maddie was a year and a half old, the novelty of having a dog was starting to wear off with Charlie and Seth. They spent less and less time with her. Even though Michael continued her morning walks, she longed for his attention on the weekends. She wasn't happy when household chores and the boy's soccer games took precedence over tummy scratches and five-mile hikes in the preserve. I lavished her with attention, but my company never seemed to measure up to the boys and Michael.

So, it came as no surprise when our ingenious puppy started to find her own entertainment. When Seth asked me to remove a piece of furniture from his room, I moved the water-proof bean bag chair to the pool deck for Maddie's new outdoor bed. She liked to flatten it by pacing in circles, hearing the crunchy noise when the small Styrofoam balls shifted to fit her body. She loved her new bunk and we often found her sprawled out laying sideways with her nose barely touching the pavement, legs shooting out the other side. I had not considered that she might find what was on the inside of a bean bag chair far more interesting than my intended use for it as a dog bed.

My underestimation of Maddie's search for amusement played out one evening when the family went for pizza. I left Maddie outside so she could enjoy a twilight swim. Returning from dinner, I walked over to the patio door and turned on the deck lights, expecting to see Maddie ready to come inside. Instead, I saw an alien from another planet covered in hundreds of white Styrofoam beads from the tip of her nose to the end of her tail. The deck had mounds of pearls looking like snowpack on a ski mountain. Thousands of little balls danced and scattered, tossed around by the wind. She had ripped the bag open, spewing the contents in a two-mile radius. Not really, but the area was a mess and the chair totaled. The task of cleaning up the debris was time consuming because the featherweight balls eluded trash bags and swirled in the air with each sweep of a broom. *Really, Lauren, blaming Maddie for tearing up the chair? Labs can be in a puppy stage for years. She's only seventeen months old. That's the kind of thing that happens when they are left to their own devices. They get into trouble. The irrigation system is going to be next.*

Over the next couple weeks, Michael and I noticed a change in her demeanor when we left the house. Maddie knew the signs signaling our departure. When we slipped into our shoes and jingled car keys, her ears would roll back and she would whine. I felt guilty walking away, leaving her standing outside the patio door.

One afternoon, after returning from work, Maddie wasn't waiting for me in her usual spot. *That's strange*, I thought. Pulling the patio door open I called, "Maddie. Maddie!" She always rushed to meet me when she heard my voice. "Where are you, Maddie girl?"

Panic set in as I ran around the pool looking for her, worried she was hurt or sick. I found her lying on the cool deck by the diving board, licking her paw. Wet and red, her front paw looked like she had been gnawing on it for a while.

Maddie lifted her head, made brief eye contact, and reverted to chewing her foot.

"Want to come inside with me?" Maddie looked past me. I knelt to pet her, looking for signs of injury.

"You're not panting. You haven't thrown up. You don't look sick. What's going on, girlfriend? Are you upset? There must be something wrong if you aren't interested in coming inside after your long day out here." I gently scooped her head in my hands, pulling her so close the warm air from her nostrils grazed my face. Maddie's ears folded in half, pinned to the sides of her head. Her sad, almond-shaped eyes evaded me. "I think it's time to find you a buddy, okay?" I said, determined to win her attention. She blinked twice, but there was no change in her expression. I took a deep breath. *Am I reading more into Maddie's behavior than I should be? Maybe, but she seems so unhappy. Spending all that time by herself, she's got to be lonely. If she's lonely, this will help her, too. Lauren, you know what to do——get her a buddy.* For the first time my worries subsided. I had a solution. I just needed Michael to approve the plan. How difficult could that be after admitting he'd seen a change in Maddie, too? *I've got this. This can be part of my final plea. He's so empathetic when it comes to Maddie, I know he'll support the idea of getting another dog. Don't get anxious about this, Lauren. Everything's going to work out.*

When Michael came home from work, I followed him into the bedroom. Before he had a chance to change into shorts and a t-shirt, I blurted out what had been bothering me all afternoon.

"I think there's something wrong with Maddie. She was acting strangely today when I got home from work. She didn't want to come inside with me and was chewing her paw. She's been sleeping more, too. Have you noticed that?"

Michael looked at me. "Can I change first before we get into this?"

"Do you think dogs suffer from depression just like people? I think we need to get another dog. Now. I'm sure she'd have no time to chew her paw if she had a new sibling. What do you think?"

Michael shot me a look that I knew only meant one thing: I was acting possessed. "If you feel that will make Maddie happy, and it's what you want to do, then I support your decision to get another puppy."

"Oh, hon, that's fantastic!" I reached out and hugged Michael. "Maddie is going to be one happy dog."

"Let's hope so."

I paused for a minute. "What do you think of adopting a shelter puppy?"

"I don't know. We've had good luck with Maddie. Why wouldn't we go back to her breeder? You know we've heard other friends' challenging stories of adopting from a care facility."

"Hon, there're a lot of homeless dogs out there that need a good home. Don't you think we should think about doing that?" I embraced the altruistic idea of adopting a dog without knowing there was a difference between a breeder puppy and a rescue. A puppy that came from a local breeder bonded with their siblings and then transitioned to an owner or family. That's dramatically different from a rescue dog that had been displaced on some level, losing its home and owner, then subjected to our county kennel where the environment can be chaotic due to the number of animals and reduced human interaction. Why didn't I think there might be behavioral consequences from that transition? I should have considered the fact that my lack of experience with rescues might cloud my better judgment.

"The last thing we need is a canine nut case coming to live with us." Michael paused. "We're having enough trouble raising Maddie. Can you imagine what might be involved in caring for a rescue?"

"Yes, I agree. I didn't think about that. Too many unknowns." I paused for a minute. "But there aren't any guarantees when buying a dog from a breeder, either. And think about what's involved in starting over with a puppy. They're a lot of work. There's potty training, and their chewing stage."

"It's obvious we need more time to think about what we want to do next. Let's not do what we did before——leap to a decision. We had no idea what we had gotten ourselves into when we brought Maddie home. She's a wonderful dog, but you have to admit she can be a drama queen at times. I have a feeling the right dog will find us. I mean, who would have ever thought you would go to work one day, see a puppy, and the next day come home with one."

"You're right about that! But I don't want to wait too long. I'm worried about Maddie." I sighed. "I don't think we should tell the boys about this conversation. The pleading might start again. I've already seen that movie."

3

DOG SHOPPING

M ichael and I pushed our decision to find another dog to the back burner. In culinary school, the back burners on the range were used to simmer chicken stock in huge steel pots over low heat for hours. The long cooking period brought out the richest flavor. I learned stock couldn't be boiled to hasten the end product. No, I had to be patient and plan ahead when making broth. What if I applied the same methodology to finding the best dog for our family? I decided to test the process. I'd take my time to locate the perfect pooch.

But before dog shopping, I had to address Maddie's lethargic behavior. Was her listlessness a result of persistent boredom? If I wanted her to engage, I had to figure out how to spark her interest. I remembered one thing that snapped Charlie and Seth out of monotony — a new toy. A couple of Matchbox cars provided hours of entertainment. Why wouldn't new toys be a good solution for Maddie, too? I put a visit to the pet store on my list of things to do.

Two days later, when I ventured out to do errands, my first stop was a pet store. The jammed parking lot should have tipped me off that there was a special event happening. Approaching the entrance, a mass of barking and jumping black, yellow, and chocolate Labrador

Retrievers came into view. There were pudgy puppies and gray-muzzled seniors in the mix, some with blocky English heads and others with long, sleek American snouts. A large sandwich board detailed information about the rescue organization that had set up camp on the sidewalk.

Every lab was tethered to a friendly person who was fostering them in their home. The volunteers were happy to share what they knew about the dog's history, temperament, and health. The playful tail-waggers being previewed for adoption wiggled torsos and yipped irresistibly.

There was a magnetic force drawing me to them. The love these canines radiated lifted my spirit. Petting and accepting sloppy kisses filled my heart with happiness. I wandered from one dog to the next as tufts of multi-colored hair became a new fashion accessory to my shorts. Tails whacked my calves and wet, pink tongues curled around my fingers.

Shocked at the exhilaration and excitement bubbling up inside me, a huge grin blossomed on my face. I laughed as the colorful bunch yapped as if to say, "Pet me, pet me." These extraordinary rescues all had a story, as did the volunteers who donated their time and effort to the cause. With my fluttering heart and sweaty hands, I bravely walked over to the desk looking for someone in charge of the event.

A young woman by the name of Julie with pretty blue eyes and hair in a ponytail spoke about the Desert Labrador Retriever Rescue with such conviction I had made up my mind to become a member before the end of the conversation.

She stepped away from the other people congregating around the desk to explain. "The organization saves almost three hundred labs a year. Many of them would have been euthanized because of limited resources. That's why we are an adoption partner for the city shelters. We also respond to calls of people ready to abandon their pet, and provide a safe place the owner can surrender the dog because of personal circumstances. We provide medical care and rehab and then match them with permanent homes." She smiled. "The mission of our organization is to educate the public about overpopulation and the importance of spaying and neutering. That's a long-term goal, of course, but that's why we fix all of our dogs before putting them up for adoption."

Three hundred saves a year. I didn't hear much after that statistic. I wanted to help preserve the lives of all those tail-waggers and lick masters.

"I'd love to become a member of this organization. Do you have any applications I could fill out right now?"

With a warm smile, she reached over to a pile of papers on the desk and handed me a two-page form. "We're always looking for new volunteers to help with the various committee responsibilities. There never seems to be enough members to fill the positions."

The opportunities seemed endless. What committee would I want to serve on? Could I be trained to be a foster or maybe host an adoption event like this one? Helping the labs transition from the rescue to their new family sounded great, but fundraisers and walking the dogs at the kennel were possibilities, too. Every assignment sounded more exciting than the last. Endorphins ricocheted inside my brain, making it difficult to focus on completing the application. I asked Julie when I might be called about the status of the submission.

"Tomorrow I'll turn in your paperwork to the volunteer coordinator. The process takes about a week to upload the information into our database. You'll probably get a call by next Monday."

"Okay," I sighed. "I'll try to be patient, but I can't wait to be part of this team."

Before walking away, I glanced over and saw they were selling bumper stickers as a fundraiser that said, "Who Rescued Who?" Weren't dogs rescued by people? I decided not to ask any questions but instead handed Julie five dollars, walked back to the car, and slapped the sticker on the trunk.

During the drive home, I couldn't stop thinking about the adorable canines showcased at the event. Even though the dogs had not come from a breeder, I was drawn to them in the same way I was to Tank, and to Maddie. After my joyful experience, I knew exactly where I wanted to dog shop——at the rescue! I had already convinced

Michael that Maddie needed a playmate. All I had to do now was persuade him that adopting a rescue was the right thing. Surely if he had seen the dogs I played with, he'd agree. With a strategy in place, I set my plan into action.

That evening I made clay pot chicken with soy sauce, ginger, garlic, allspice berries, and fresh squeezed orange juice. The kids always agreed the best part of the dish was the gravy served over steamed rice, so I made sure there would be no shortage of the rich aromatic sauce. While everyone was diving into their first bite, I dove into the conversation I had been anticipating.

"I found a toy for Maddie today at our favorite pet store. I think she's really going to like it." I paused before blurting out, "I also met a bunch of amazing labs that were hanging out in front of the store. A lab rescue was hosting an adoption event. There must have been ten dogs——all colors and ages, puppies to adults. They were as cute and friendly as they could possibly be." I looked around the table. "I played with all of them."

"I'm surprised you didn't come home with one." Seth laughed. "Would you adopt a rescue?" A smile emerged on his face.

"Mmmm, maybe. Dad and I haven't been totally on board about rescues. I don't know, do you think you'd be open to it?" I looked at Michael.

"It's not that I'm opposed to a rescue, it's just that I don't know much about them. I mean, two years ago, we didn't even have a dog," Michael replied hesitantly.

"Well, we do now, and speaking of Maddie, I think we all are in agreement that she needs a playmate." Everyone nodded as I continued my argument. "A volunteer for the rescue told me they adopt out three hundred dogs a year. That's a lot of labs that are looking for new owners and if we want to help reduce the number of homeless pets——"

"Wait a minute," Michael interrupted. "You're moving way too fast on this rescue thing. Maybe we should give it a little more thought before we make a decision?"

"The dogs at the event were great. I couldn't find anything wrong with them. They were well behaved and looked healthy." I had to slow down. In my attempt to sound convincing, I sounded like a used car salesperson. "Sorry, I'm really excited. I think this might be the perfect fit for us. We could even let the organization know our preference of sex and color." I raised my eyebrows. "And, if we wanted to consider getting an older dog, we could do that, too. Wouldn't it be nice not to have to go through the puppy phase again? You know, stuff like letting them out in the middle of the night when they have to pee and living through their chewing stage?"

"Okay, I'll tell you what, why don't we all go to the next event and check them out?"

"Great idea, Dad," Charlie said.

"I'll ask about their schedule. These dogs are really special, guys. Can't wait for the next event." With new confidence, I pushed back on my seat before continuing. "Now that we have that settled, there is one more topic to discuss. Do you remember how much you guys wanted a dog?"

"Yeah," Charlie answered.

"When we first brought Maddie home you played with her and gave her lots of attention. But as time went by you seemed to lose interest in taking care of her. Right?"

"Maybe a little, but we still take her on walks and swim with her in the pool," Seth said. "We pick up her poop and feed her," he hesitated. "Sometimes."

"Sometimes isn't enough. Are you in?"

"Alright," Seth replied.

"Charlie, you haven't said much. I need your commitment, too."

"I'll help out. I really want another dog and it'll be great for Maddie to have somebody to keep her company. Now that we've solved the problems of the world, where's dessert?"

The next morning as Michael and I cleared the dishes from brunch, he cleared his throat and looked at me.

"Hey, I know I've been a little hard on you about this whole adoption issue." I stopped and raised my eyebrows. "It's not that I'm upset with you or against the idea of a rescue, it's just that I haven't had any experience with them. Yesterday you saw how a rescue operation works and had fun playing with all the different dogs. I know I'd feel better about the whole thing if I could do the same thing you did. So, I did a little research of my own this morning. DLRR is hosting another adoption event today. What do you say we go together and check it out?"

I put the dishes in the sink and reached out to hug him. "Oh honey, I'd love to do that!" Michael gave me a squeeze.

His eyes twinkled. "And then I thought we could stop at the library and pick up a couple books on dog adoption."

"Sounds like the perfect Sunday afternoon to me."

Later that evening, the family gathered around the dinner table for Thai Massaman curry stir-fry with shrimp, zucchini and mushrooms, and side dishes of brown rice and green papaya salad.

"Mom, this is so good," Seth said. "I didn't think I liked shrimp."

"Glad you like it. Thanks for trying it."

"Hon, you seem to have a way of convincing all of us to try a lot of things we think we don't like. For example, going to the rescue event today." Michael winked at me.

I gave Michael a quizzical look. "Now, wait a minute. It was your idea to go."

"I'm just kidding. It's true. I wasn't excited about the idea of getting involved with a rescue but having met the Desert Lab members today, I'm thinking a little differently about the whole thing. They were so professional and the level of dedication the volunteers have toward both the organization and the dogs they're fostering is impressive. As for the labs, they were nothing short of amazing. They were all colors and ages, each with their own unique story the fosters were open to sharing." He looked at the boys. "Now I know why Mom got hooked."

"Did you get to play with them?" Charlie asked.

"All seven of them. Good thing our application wasn't approved, or we might have come home with one."

"Darn, that would have been so cool," Seth said excitedly.

"I wish I went with you. That sounds like it was fun," Charlie added.

"It really was. I know I wasn't too excited about getting a rescue, but this DLRR group convinced me, just like Mom, that adopting a homeless dog is the right thing to do."

The next week, I jumped every time the phone rang, hoping my membership had been approved. Finally, the anticipated phone call came.

"Hi Lauren, this is Sandra from Desert Labrador Retriever Rescue. Your membership application has been approved. We're thrilled to have you on our team. Have you thought about what committee you'd like to serve on?"

"I'm so happy to hear from you. Thanks for getting back to me. I'm looking forward to volunteering. Where do you need assistance the most?"

"It would probably be walking the newly-acquired dogs housed at our kennel. We have volunteers called shelter walkers who visit the city animal facilities and evaluate the labs that are on the euthanasia list. With the help of the animal services staff our member interacts with the dogs one-on-one to determine whether they have issues like aggression. That way we know which ones we can re-home. After the paperwork is completed for the transfer, one of our volunteers picks them up and drives them to our kennel. I know you're anxious to get started and we rarely have enough dog walkers. It'd be great if you could do that. I'll email you the volunteer manual that explains the responsibilities of the other committees, too. Take a look at it. Maybe there's something else that interests you as well."

"No, I think walking the new intakes sounds perfect."

"And Lauren, remember, if you want to adopt from us, you'll need to schedule a home visit and get approved by one of our home visit committee members."

"Okay, good to know, but for right now I'm just excited about volunteering."

I couldn't wait to be near the dogs. While jotting the information from Sandra, I daydreamed of serene walks in the park, joyful belly rubs under shade trees, and the lavished one-on-one attention that would make the new intakes feel loved. I was at the crossroads of these canines beginning their transition from abandonment to adoption.

But those idyllic visions faded as a nagging sense of anxiety tempered my excitement. What did I know about rescue dogs? Nothing. I had no training, no prior experience, and yet I was going to show up at a facility and walk a bunch of their newly saved dogs. My hands tingled, breaking into a sweat. I took a deep breath. *Lauren, simply snap on a leash and take each dog for a spin around the block.*

I feared I'd be interacting with emotionally broken canines that lost their family members, suffered physical illness, or had depression from being housed at a shelter for weeks on end. Ohhh, that sounded terrible. I couldn't think about that. I had committed to walking the dogs and writing a few notes in the file about their behavior. Reneging on my first assignment wasn't a viable option.

Feeling overwhelmed without even having stepped foot in the kennel, I called Patti, the intake coordinator, and asked her to meet me at the facility for basic training. That night I fell asleep with the volunteer training manual on my chest and dreamt I was chasing after a lab, running toward a busy city street, my sides needled with sharp pains, yelling, "Come back, come back!"

The next morning, I shook loose the cobwebs lodged in my head, trying to erase the bad dreams. With a protein shake in hand, I headed out the door and entered the address on the GPS. Singing to the country music blaring on the radio, the twenty-five- minute drive went by quickly. I almost missed the turn into the building's parking lot. Following Sandra's instructions, I drove to the back of the facility and looked for the unmarked silver door. I entered the code on the box beside the door, stood back, and waited until I heard the lock unclick, my cue to enter.

The smell of animals, disinfectants, and antiseptics bombarded my nostrils, the howling and woofing rattled my ears, and the polished white floors blinded me. I stood transfixed for a minute and then followed the crescendo of noise down the corridor.

The hallway merged into a spacious room with two rows of stacked wire mesh crates along the back wall containing dogs in all shapes, sizes, and colors. Scanning the area, I couldn't spot one Labrador Retriever. Could I be in the wrong place? Barely able to hear someone calling me over the din, I turned and saw Patti, a stocky blonde with coral lipstick sporting a friendly smile.

"Lauren, over here." Patti waved her hand. "I've been waiting for you."

I hurried over to where she was seated at a small desk scattered with papers and folders. She stood up, shook my hand, and said loudly, "Welcome. Nice to meet you. I know it seems kind of confusing and completely overwhelming when you enter this place." Pointing to a blue door behind her desk, she added, "We rent six kennels that are in a separate area for our intakes from the city shelter. This clinic provides spay and neuter service to the general public. The dogs and cats in this room are here to be altered. The owner of the company is supportive of our mission and provides this temporary space for our rescues to stay until we place them in foster care. The staff examine and treat our incoming dogs with veterinary services, giving them vaccines and spaying or neutering if needed. Their employees give medication and walk our dogs when they have time, but clinic responsibilities come first." She paused to take a drink from her water bottle. "That's why we need dog walking volunteers. We'd like our dogs to be their first priority with the clinic, but we're just grateful to have this facility——they charge us reduced rates and lower our costly vet expenses. Some of the dogs we intake have medical issues."

I gave Patti a thumbs up, understanding for the first time why the organization would choose to share the chaotic, frenzied environment. Over the ruckus, she instructed me how to leash a dog and fill out the paperwork, making notes on the health and personality characteristics of each dog I walked. The information would help determine the appropriate foster care placement because a majority of the intakes came to the organization with little or no prior history. The volunteer walkers were asked to share what they observed about the dog's disposition, physical status, and knowledge of commands.

"Oh, and be on the lookout for signs of separation anxiety, too.

Like excessive barking, panting, and restlessness. Sometimes called "Velcro-dogs" because they stick close by your side, they look for constant interaction to make them feel loved and cared for. They don't want to be left alone; a glimpse of their kennel can trigger a doggie break down. You'll have a fight on your hands when trying to get them to re-enter their kennel, but just because they don't want to go back into their cage doesn't necessarily mean they have separation anxiety. That's where you come in." She looked at me with hopeful eyes. "If volunteers like you report the dog has symptoms of the condition, we know to look for an adopter who will be home with the dog for a couple months and is committed to a rigorous exercise plan. We see a higher return rate without a plan like that in place because of problems the dogs cause while the owners are away."

"Geez. That sounds terrible for the dog and owner. There must be a way to help a dog with that condition."

"There's no cure for separation anxiety. That's one of the reasons our adopters feel frustrated. I've heard of window shades torn down, peeing and pooping in the house, drywall chewed off, furniture legs whittled down to the size of a pencil, and ingestion of anything in sight whether edible or not, including Brillo pads. But, one thing we have learned is that exercise tends to lessen their anxiety. A tired lab is a good lab. That's why we are diligent in matching them with an owner who will participate in some sort of physical activity every day."

"How many of the rescues we adopt out have separation anxiety?"

"Oh, I don't know. Maybe twenty percent. The condition comes in degrees of severity. Our adopters as a whole are very tolerant and tend to work with their new addition if the condition is mild or medium. The highly destructive dogs that are difficult to treat end up back on our doorstep. Sometimes we have our vet dispense a doggie anti-depressant or some other type of anti-anxiety medication to calm them down. That's a last resort, however, because the medications can have side effects."

"Wow," I sighed. "I don't think I could own that kind of dog."

"Well, not your worry, you're here to walk the dogs." Patti looked at me, reiterated taking one dog at a time, then passed me a leash and pointed in the direction of a blue door.

"Don't forget to take a poop bag along," she called out behind me. "We don't want any complaints from the owner of the clinic that we aren't picking up after our dogs."

4

SPINNING OUT OF CONTROL

W ith a pounding heart, I pried the door open. As I stepped into the small room, the racket of rapid-fire barking sounded like machine guns. All five rectangular chain-link cages housed a Labrador Retriever, but I didn't know where to look first because the collective, high-pitched barking bounced off the concrete floor and tiled walls. The ring in my ears reminded me of the aftermath of a rock concert.

I felt lightheaded and seriously considered retreating to the car. This was not the serene experience I had envisioned——it was sheer bedlam. I had no interest in trying to sort out such an unruly environment.

My eyes made what I thought would be one last sweep of the cages before leaving. But in that split second, the dog in the third kennel captured my attention. Coy and curious, he stood erect, with ears perched forward. I couldn't look away from his eyes. He pressed his nose through the chain-link fence, popping it through a hole. As he tried to catch my scent, his nostrils flared in and out. When I took one step forward, he pulled his nose out of the fence and spun like a supersonic top defying the laws of gravity.

He darted in tight circles, rebounding off the narrow walls. I gawked at him, watching his body leap into the air, landing with the certainty of a cat. His dance only slowed to a stop when a forceful, dry cough caused him to gag. Unfazed, he lifted his bowed head, flashed his eyes, and pushed off on four feet, making his ears flop front to back. He looked like a rocking horse ready to snap off its springs. If his goal was to out-bark every other dog, he succeeded. I covered my ears and stared in amazement as I read the plaque posted over his kennel: *Shadow, neutered eleven-month-old male. Intake date, August eighth. Dispense oral antibiotic medication three times a day for kennel cough.*

What? No other details? Surely there had to be more information listed about him. I suspected they didn't use the word "possessed" for fear of intimidating newbies in the organization like me.

Mesmerized by such unusual behavior, I walked closer, expecting the frenzied dance to continue. Instead, I witnessed a complete metamorphosis. He sat perfectly still. He didn't even blink, focusing every ounce of energy on staying connected with me. All the distractions of noise and commotion faded away as an emotional energy field pulled me with such force that all I could do was focus on him.

His jet-black coat looked as if it had been dipped in clear varnish. His fur shimmered as he slowly shifted from one front paw to the other, back and forth. I felt as though his eyes were looking into the window of my soul. He lowered his head to get a clearer view of my face through the fencing. Shadow held my full attention. The mischievous gleam in his eye, his perked-up ears, and his head cocking from left to right grabbed my attention, rendering me unable to walk away from his overwhelming personality. It was only when he lifted one paw and hit the chain-link fence, making it clatter, that I snapped back into reality, remembering I had come to the kennel to walk the dogs.

He continued to stare at me. *"Why did you take so long to come over here?"*

I leaned in closer. "Did you just say something to me? No, that's not possible. Or is it?"

His entire body lifted off the ground as he began his dance again, but I couldn't stop watching the show he was putting on. His final act concluded by hitting the edge of the silver dishes, dumping food and water all over the floor. He lunged to extricate himself from the puddle of soggy food nuggets, but one foot landed in the bowl, causing kibbles to dance around the cage. Shadow's ears swooped from side to side, temporarily blinding his sight line. He swerved to avoid the dish, narrowly missing a head-on collision with the fence.

I stood back in awe. He was like a Tasmanian Devil and I was caught up in the whirlwind. Who was this dog? Where did he come from and why was he so insistent on getting my attention? Did he do this with all the dog walkers? I wanted to know everything about him.

I dismissed the thought that Shadow demonstrated the gyrations he had just performed for everyone walking into the kennel. No, I needed to believe he had chosen me to be his one-person audience. I wanted to be special. The magnetic connection between us piqued my curiosity. How could I feel an emotional attachment to a dog I had only met two minutes ago? There were sparks shooting back and forth. Was it my imagination or could we understand each other's responses?

Foolishly thinking I could decipher his character, I continued to look into his eyes. He had a personality that was so compelling it filled the entire kennel. I was spell-bound. If I thought rationally about my encounter with Shadow, it would have been easy for me to walk away, knowing he was, indeed, a handful. But I didn't. I let my feelings override my better judgment.

My euphoria evaporated with the thought that Shadow could be adopted by someone else. I worried he could be placed in a foster home at any moment. What if they did that tomorrow? What if I never saw him again? Why was I acting like this? I felt panicky. My heart beat so loudly I could feel the pounding in my ears.

I couldn't imagine him being with anyone other than me. I envisioned him at our house with Maddie, the kids, and Michael. I could see the blissful adventures we would share. What was happening? Why was my brain having these thoughts? In my stomach, there were a thousand butterflies taking flight. My body was being hijacked by a host of euphoric feelings. Was it possible I could be falling in love with a dog? Yup! It was too late. Shadow had won me over. *Lauren, breathe. Breathe.* I took a deep breath.

After a few minutes, I regained my composure and scanned the next two kennels to see a pretty yellow female, sweet Rhea, curled up on her matted towels, and dark-eyed, timid, black-coated Kippy, who melted into a puddle on the floor as I passed by. Glancing at the first kennel, I spotted a spunky, chocolate-colored lab named Lightning, wagging her tail so hard I thought it might fall off. Finally, there was the yellow lab Lucky, who pranced around his cage, springing from paw to paw. But none of them begged further investigation, thanks to Shadow's continued staring.

Common sense might have told me to pick the one who looked the easiest to handle for my first dog walking experience. But any semblance of common sense was kicked to the door the moment Shadow wiggled into my heart. I found myself boldly heading toward his kennel. I threw caution to the wind, ignoring the potential consequences of taking the spirited canine for a short walk, knowing the real issue was the forever walk I wanted him to take with me. What? Huh? Shaking my head trying to expel the irrational thoughts from my brain only led to more questions crowding in.

"No, no, no," I said under my breath. I was reading far more into what happened than I should.

Why couldn't I drop the whole topic of adoption and focus my attention on walking the dogs? Because I wanted to believe more than anything in that moment that Shadow had picked me out of all the other volunteers to be his champion. *Lauren, his champion. Really?* Wow, that dog had cast some sort of magical spell. But I loved his attentiveness, his passion to connect with me, and his stunningly handsome face. He could have been a centerfold for a lab calendar. I tried to ignore the thumping of my heart.

5

FREEDOM'S THRESHOLD

With leash in hand, I approached Shadow's kennel, listening to another outburst of his unbridled barking and snorting.

"Shadow, if you want to go for a walk you've got to stop barking."

"Too excited."

"You're not going to run me over, are you?"

"Fat chance."

I knelt to unlatch the door. Bam! It swung back on its hinge, hitting me with a blow that propelled me backwards onto the floor. Ambushed by a rocket of black fur, I stayed in a prone position and watched him clear my body in one leap, racing toward the exit. Thank goodness the door was closed.

It took me several minutes to catch him, as he decided to use the area in front of the kennels as a dog run, causing the others to bark frantically. He was panting wildly when I finally lassoed him with the leash and pulled him close enough to pet his silky-smooth head.

"Hurry. Need to pee."

He let out a yowl as I held his thrashing head, snapping on the leash in a move straight out of a wrestling championship. Once Shadow knew where he was headed, he almost ripped my arm out of its socket leading me toward the door, barking and throwing himself into the air. Exiting the building, he found the closest bush and peed. Only then did his anxiety begin to subside. He strained against the leash, pulling me down the sidewalk and stopping abruptly to repeatedly dip his head toward the ground, coughing and gagging wildly. *"Honk, honk."*

"You sound like a goose——that's really bad. You okay, boy? That choking noise is terrible." I knelt on the sidewalk and placed my hands around his chest to give him a chance to catch his breath. "I know you want to keep going, but..."

"Don't want to stop." Shadow lunged forward, almost pulling me over.

"Don't worry, we'll get to the park. Only one more block to go. But you have to stop barking. I don't want your kennel cough to get worse."

We walked a little further until reaching a busy intersection. "Okay, Shadow, we've got to hustle to get across while the light's green." Forcing him to jog intensified his cough, slowing him to a dead stop in the middle of the intersection. The hand signal on the traffic light flashed orange.

"Shadow, let's go, we're going to be run over." Could I pick up a seventy-pound dog and carry him to safety? The light was changing. Motorists stacked up at the intersection watched me struggle with a dog barely able to walk. "Shadow, hurry." I waved my hand frantically from side to side at the faces behind the wheel. The light changed to green. A car started toward us.

"Wait, wait, I have a sick dog!" I yelled. The car stopped. I leaned down, wrapped my arms around Shadow's chest and dragged him to the sidewalk. I turned and blew kisses to all the drivers for not killing us, then collapsed on the ground. "Geez, Shadow, that was close. I didn't know you were so sick."

"Me neither."

Sweat trickled down my back. The temperature had reached 110 degrees, but that wasn't the only reason I sported a drenched shirt.

I flinched every time Shadow coughed on our way to the park. I didn't know how to stop his hacking, and I felt guilty for making his condition worse. The white plastic band around his neck, which signified he had been placed on the twenty-four-hour euthanasia list because he had caught kennel cough at the shelter, was disturbing. Even though intellectually I understood the condition was highly transmittable and put other shelter dogs at risk, the thought of how close he had come to death raised goose bumps on my arms.

When we arrived at the field, the warm breeze tickled his ears, causing repetitive head shakes. He lunged, darting to the right and left, his feverish pace continuing as if disentangling demons.

"You've got to slow down, buddy. You're panting really hard. Let's find a place to rest for a couple minutes." The soft grassy area under the shade of a leafy ash tree seemed like the perfect place to take a break. A huge sigh of relief escaped as I sat down.

"Out of the kennel. Yay!" He yipped several times as if chastising me for sitting before finally taking a dive, bumping into my side. For a brief moment, I felt the warmth of his fur against my legs and the weight of his muzzle in my lap.

"Grass, trees, walk, freedom."

My fingertips caressed his torso. While I dreamily studied every expression, gesture, and physical characteristic, I wondered why he was homeless.

"Bunny?"

His eyes flashed, and his tail lifted into the air. He took a dive. As I fell forward hanging on to the leash, my elbows skidded over the grass and my arms tingled from the strain of holding him back. With wide eyes, he watched the cottontail hop off into the distance. The collar tightened around his neck with his repeated attempts to break free, provoking another round of gags.

"You're okay." I reached out to pet him in long gentle strokes, hoping he wouldn't sense how much his cough scared me. "That rabbit is causing all kinds of trouble, huh?"

"Tastes like chicken."

His glossy charcoal coat shimmered in the sunlight. He was tall and lanky, but his sculpted muscular chest confirmed he was an athlete. He felt lean and ruggedly strong when I ran my hand down his back and over his arched tail. When my hand dropped into my lap, he nosed it with his long, sleek American muzzle.

"Don't stop."

"Shadow, you are one beautiful dog. I don't know why anyone would give you up." I watched his eyes soften and ears pop up on top of his head as if they were spring-loaded. "Are you flirting with me?"

Shadow's tail gently wagged as he pranced around me in wide circles. His peeled back lips revealed pearly whites and a happy smile. I tried to transfer the lead from one hand to the other to stop the leash from tangling, but after several rounds I looked like a fly in a spider's web. He sat and looked fixedly at me, throwing his cumbersome but soft paw over my arm. *"Pet me."* His ears rotated backward and his eyes, shaped like almonds, danced. I felt a wave of gratitude knowing he was safe in the hands of our rescue.

I glanced at my watch. "Oh my gosh, it's two o'clock and I haven't walked any of the other dogs. I need to take you back."

"Don't want to."

"Let's go."

We ambled back to the facility to avoid a coughing spell. Arriving at the kennel, the familiar piercing streams of barks went into overdrive. I tightened up the leash, walked over to Shadow's cage, and opened the door.

"Okay, in you go."

"Not interested."

I leaned forward with the leash, directing him to enter the space while pushing his hind end with my legs. Shadow, determined not to cross the steel bar at the base of the kennel, sat on my feet. He wasn't going to budge an inch. Unable to muscle him into the area, I dropped the leash and looked around the room for options. A bag of treats and leashes were draped over an empty kennel. I walked over and picked up the bag. Shadow's ears pricked forward.

"How would you like one of these?" I asked, pulling out one of the milk bones.

"Treat? I know down, stop, come, stay, off, drop, sit, shake, roll over."

I threw two of them in the back of his kennel and shut the door before he could seize them.

"Shadow, do you see these treats? There's only one way to get them." He looked at me and then at the two bones. I unleashed his collar and opened the entry way. As he bolted in, I closed off the escape route behind him, watching him scarf the goodies in seconds.

"Hey, not fair." He pawed at the chain link fencing.

"I'm sorry, but I didn't know how else to get you back in." I gazed at his droopy eyes and rolled back ears. Oh, how I wanted to throw my arms around him and give him a hug. But I couldn't. I had to take Kippy, Lucky, Lightning, and Rhea out for a walk.

Every time I returned with another dog from our stroll around the park, Shadow barked with such force his ears flopped back and forth. Before leaving, I checked all the latches on the kennels, pausing at Shadow's to wiggle my fingers inside the chain link to say good-bye. As I pushed the blue door open to exit, a thunderous woof stopped me.

"Come back, come back."

I looked over at the third kennel. Shadow cocked his head, right, left, right. My heart melted.

The next day, I returned to the facility under the guise of walking the dogs, but the real reason was to spend more time with Shadow. Remembering my first encounter, I decided to try a new tactic. I walked Kippy, Lucky, Lightning and Rhea before turning my attention to him.

He acted like a child having a full-blown temper tantrum, barking with such force his whole body lifted off the ground. *"Want out. Now."*

Had I made a bad decision making him wait? I was about to find out. I silently faced his kennel and stepped as far left as possible while still being able to reach the hinge on the right side of the door. Slowly, I flicked up the latch with my right hand, letting the door swing open to cover my body like a protective shield. As feared, he shot out like a cannon, darting into the middle of the room. I only had temporary asylum from the Tasmanian Devil because the door swung back after he hit it with his paws, slamming me into the adjacent kennel.

He raced back and forth on the stretch of concrete in front of the occupied kennels, snorting and throwing himself to the ground on his front paws. His jaw quivered and teeth chattered as he darted past me at breakneck speed. I waited patiently until he wandered over to my feet, plopped down, and eagerly offered his neck for a scratch. I snapped on the leash and we headed outside.

Thankfully, his kennel cough had improved enough that we could cross the intersection without incident. I extended his walk to three loops around the park using the excuse that he needed exercise to help clear his lungs of lingering mucus, but my real motive was just to spend time with him. He panted laboriously, the afternoon sun scorching his black coat. I veered off the path and headed toward the shade of an ash tree.

"C'mon boy. Let's take a break."

I sat, pulling him toward me. Within seconds, his long narrow tongue began making its way across my exposed arms. His sticky saliva prompted me to push him away.

"Let's go."

"Stop. We just sat down."

"No, you sat down."

Shadow, obviously unhappy that I had curtailed his walk, barked with such force that all his paws left the ground. With this comedic outburst of defiance, I giggled and rolled into a tucked position, lacing my hands around my knees. He persisted in trying to find a way to reach my face by digging his snout between my arms and ears. The combination of his yips of excitement and repetitive nose dives made it impossible not to laugh. He twisted his muzzle underneath my elbow and pried me open like a shucked oyster. His clever tactics won him face access and a piece of my heart.

"Okay, okay. We'll go. Soon. Shadow, down."

He rotated his body backwards and then dropped onto the grass.

"Good dog, Shadow. So, you know at least one command. That's great." I stood, looked him in the eye and raised my palm in the air. "Shadow, sit." He popped up into a sitting position. "Good dog, Shadow," I said, giving him a scratch under the neck. "Shadow, sta…"

"I'm done."

"Shadow, calm down. That loud bark of yours has to go."

"Why?"

"Shadow! Quiet."

"Okay."

We sat under the tree watching blades of grass dance in the wind. I absent-mindedly floated my hand over the top of his head and then leaned in to scratch his neck. His muzzle melted on top of my hand.

"Like that."

"Feels good, huh? Well, that will have to do for now because I have to take you back."

"Just one more scratch?"

"Let's go," I said, tugging the leash. He slowly followed my lead. The thought of returning Shadow to the clinic spurred a renewal of my worries. What if I returned to the facility in two days to walk the dogs and found Shadow's kennel empty, the intake sign removed? I hated that thought. I stopped mid-stride, unable to take another step. Shadow bumped into my calves. Bending over, I reached under his belly, picked his front paws off the sidewalk, and drew him close to my chest, laying the side of my face on his fur. I could hear his heart beating in tandem with mine. *C'mon, Lauren, think rationally. How can I possibly get attached to a dog after interacting with him for only two hours? Put him down and get moving.*

He slowed his step when we neared the facility entrance. Gathering up his leash, I led him across the threshold that restricted his freedom. We passed the animals waiting to be neutered and joined the other labs in our rescue area. He lagged behind, seeing his cage come into view.

"Okay, time to go back into your kennel," I said, pulling him by the collar.

"Don't want to." He anchored his weight on his back legs.

"I'm sorry, I have to do this." My voice cracked as I forced him into the kennel he loathed. Looking at Shadow's penetrating eyes, I felt despondent. Kneeling on the concrete floor, I squeezed my fingers through the links, wanting to touch his velvet fur and feel the warmth of his body one more time. We were face-to-face, staring at each other. He gently licked my exposed fingertips. In that moment, I knew Shadow had found his forever home with us.

That evening, I called and scheduled a home visit for the following day, pleading my case to move Shadow out of the boarding facility as soon as possible to hasten his recovery from kennel cough.

The next morning, we all popped out of bed and scurried around the house as if we were putting the house up for sale. Michael and I bathed Maddie and brushed her until her coat glistened. Although I considered putting a tiara on Maddie's head, because of her queen-like status, I decided it might be a bit much. We were all ready when Karen, a petite brunette with a pixie cut, arrived at noon. She was upbeat and friendly as she toured the house, noting physical details about the property and interacting with each of us.

"Karen, I really appreciate you coming over on such short notice. I know it usually takes a few more days to set up an appointment."

"I'm glad I could help you out. I'm sure you're wondering when you'll hear back from me."

"Yes, I'd love to know that."

"Let me see what I can do this afternoon to get the report pushed through admin."

"Thanks. I'll keep checking my computer tonight. It was nice to meet you."

"I enjoyed meeting your family, too."

Later that evening, after receiving the approval to adopt, I ran around the house ecstatically informing each family member about the good news. Then I called Patti to let her know I wanted to adopt Shadow. I couldn't risk waiting one more minute knowing he could be paired with another household with just one phone call.

I tossed and turned all night, knowing Shadow's destiny was to be part of our family. I woke up at five-thirty, groggy and exhausted but euphoric. He had worked his magic on me. The four-legged black knight had swept me off my feet, pledging his love. I hoped Michael wouldn't be jealous and that the boys wouldn't be disappointed I was bringing a very large puppy home.

6

JUMPING OFF A CLIFF

The decision to assume responsibility as Shadow's new owner excited and terrified me. I threw caution to the wind in choosing to adopt him, embarking on an adventure into the world of dog rescue. A war raged inside my head as the spontaneous side of me bubbled up, anticipating the challenges of making him part of our household, but the fearful side worried what the consequences of that choice might be. *Lauren, remember. I have an out in this deal. Patti told me I can return him to the organization in twenty-one days if he isn't a fit for the family. But why would I need an out if I'm going to give it one hundred percent? Geez, what am I thinking? How can I commit to something I have no idea what I'm committing to?* The push of success and the pull of failure washed over me.

The day to bring Shadow home arrived and despite lack of sleep and restless dreams, a jolt of energy ripped through me like I had consumed too many espresso shots. As I drove to the intake coordinator's house to meet Patti and finalize the adoption, conflicting thoughts tangled in my brain, conjuring questions with no immediate answers. Had I been too hasty in my decision to make Shadow part of our family? I had only walked him twice and spent two hours with him. Did I lack the knowledge and experience to re-home a rescue dog? What if I turned out to be a lousy adopter? What if he broke loose and ran away? *Stop thinking and pay atten...* I looked out the window. Darn. I had already driven past her house. I turned around and headed back to Patti's white stucco house. She waved as I pulled into the driveway.

I smiled and chirped, "Hi Patti," trying to put on an air of confidence. "Thanks for scrambling to get the paperwork together on such short notice. How are you?"

"I'm great," she replied. "I could do these adoption packets in my sleep——I've done a lot of them over the last ten years. I love this part of the process. Signing the admin docs are the final step before our rescues join their new families. I know how anxious you are to get Shadow out of the kennel. Are you ready to make this official?"

"Yes, I'm excited. But a little nervous, too."

"Don't worry, you'll figure out what to do."

She handed me the folder. "Just need your signature and the adoption fee."

I pulled the document from the folder and scanned the printed pages. The form looked familiar because I had reviewed the adoption contract in the volunteer manual. So why were the sweat glands in my hands going into overdrive? The reality of accepting responsibility for Shadow was triggering anxiety. *Lauren, stop acting so excitable and just sign the darn thing. I'm overreacting again, it's no big deal to adopt a dog. People do it all the time.*

Rummaging inside my purse, I found a pen and pulled a check from my wallet. I signed the forms and handed her the payment.

Patti glanced at the check and said, "Thank you for the extra contribution. Our budget is running tight this year because of high vet bills. Here's his medical file and medication for his kennel cough." She reached into her pocket and offered up a green bottle of pills.

I looked at her with a blind stare. "I don't know a lot about kennel cough other than it's highly contagious. You can imagine how concerned I was witnessing it for the first time with Shadow. He coughed to the point of choking when I walked him. The loud hacking was scary——he sounded like a goose." I decided not to mention the incident crossing the street.

"Yes, that can be one of the symptoms. I wouldn't worry too much. Dogs kept in a boarding kennel pick up respiratory bronchitis from other coughing dogs sharing the same space. But he's been on an antibiotic for several days, so he won't pass it to your other dog. Plus, he's going to get rest, and be in a healthy home environment, so I think he'll be back to normal in less than a week."

The word 'normal' struck me as being so ridiculous I burst into an uneasy laugh. "Normal? Will Shadow ever be normal?" We couldn't possibly be talking about the same dog.

"He'll be fine," Patti assured me.

Shadow most likely suffered emotional and physical setbacks from being unloved and then abandoned. Although animal services rescued him from the city streets, being housed in a foreign kennel at the county shelter for numerous weeks compounded his erratic behavior. There was no denying his Tasmanian behavior and case of kennel cough yielded a worrisome combination. *Don't go there, Lauren. Worrying about what might happen when he comes to live with us isn't helpful. Shadow's old life is going to be a distant memory.*

Focusing on his life and the promise of a dazzling future eased my worries. After the relentless hours I would work with him while bathing him in love, he would transform into a mentally stable and emotionally grounded dog. I would extinguish his fears and restore him to greatness. I saw myself as Shadow's heroine. *His heroine? Wow Lauren, that's wishful thinking.*

"Lauren. Lauren? Hey, I lost you," Patti said.

"Sorry. I was just thinking. I'm committed to make this adoption work, but as you know, Shadow could turn out to be a wild card. I don't know what I am getting myself into, or maybe I do and that's what scares me. I only have twenty-one days to determine whether he's a match for our family and figure out his disposition——that's ambitious, don't you think?"

Patti raised her eyebrows.

I raised mine, too. "After witnessing his behavior at the kennel, I know that Shadow may very well be a lifetime project. Who would want that kind of challenge when adopting a dog?"

"You'd be surprised. We have some pretty special adopters," Patti commented.

"I'm sure. Let's hope I'm one of them. You have my word that I'll do everything in my power to keep him."

I worried that failed adoptions resulted in the dog and adopter suffering emotional and mental hardships. The dog, returned to a foster home or shelter, harbored the mounting stress from numerous transitions to new owners, households and routines. The adopter experienced guilt and loss from not being able to integrate the dog into the household. I wanted no part of being a failed adoption statistic, and as I was about to find out, neither did Patti.

"Do you have a crate for Shadow?" she asked.

"Mmm, no."

"And you're going to pick him up now, right?"

"I was going to. I mean I'd like to," I said, fumbling to find the right words.

She put her hands on her hips. "How are you going to transport him to the house?"

"I planned to wrap the leash around one of the head rests of the car to make sure he's tied to the seat."

Patti scrunched up her face and cocked her head sideways. "Do you think that's going to work? I want both of you to arrive safely. You haven't had him in a car yet, have you?"

"No. But the house is just twenty-five minutes away. Don't you think the leash will hold him in place?" My voice trailed off realizing how foolish I sounded.

Patti broke the silence. "Why don't you take one of the crates I have in the garage? You may need it, and not just for the car. You'll have peace of mind knowing he can't get into anything when you leave the house. Rescues like Shadow can create some problems at first when unsupervised inside a house. There can't be any harm in using it until you get to know him a bit better, right? I always recommend crate training for our rescues when a dog's character is in question."

Instead of arguing about taking the crate, I kept my mouth shut, worried what Patti might say about my inexperience with rescues like Shadow. I didn't want a lecture on using a crate to manage a dog that might have behavioral issues. What I wanted was a hug and a couple of reassuring words to fortify my confidence that I would be able to handle whatever was about to ensue. I looked at the ground and nervously shuffled dirt over my sneakers.

"Okay, that's probably a good idea. Thank you. I hope he settles down once I get him home. I may call for some guidance."

"Of course you can call, but I'm on the phone a lot handling these intakes," she replied. "Just leave a message. I'll get back to you as soon as I can. You'll make it work. Getting him into a routine with daily exercise will help him calm down. Don't forget you wanted a special dog. I feel certain you found one. And if you need the name of a trainer, let me know."

I heaved the cumbersome airline crate into the back of my car, thanked Patti, and headed off to pick up Shadow.

My heart raced as I mapped out a strategy for introducing Shadow into our household. Strategy? I had no idea what my next moves were beyond checking him out of the facility.

7

KENNEL BREAK

The parking lot had a spot available by a row of bushes, perfect for Shadow to pee on before our drive home. Slamming the car door with one hand, I looked down and realized that the other one was shaking. The newly purchased leash slipped through my fingers, cascading to the asphalt. I picked it up and entered the code to the building, but the door hinge squeaked, setting off a chain reaction of frenzied barking. I needed to focus on retrieving Shadow from the facility, but the decibel level was equivalent to an aircraft carrier, punishing my eardrums. I wondered how any dog could live in this chaotic environment and not be emotionally traumatized.

I tried blocking out the piercing bark, bark, woof echoing off the walls. Walking over to his kennel, I released the latch and carefully reached in with one arm, attempting to snap on the leash. I spoke calmly to Shadow, but high-pitched yelps and thunderous booms drowned out my voice. With the door slightly ajar, Shadow saw an opportunity to make his jail break. He rammed his body against the kennel door, forcing it to swing open, and leaped out.

"Back again? Yay!"

"Aaaaaa——you silly dog," I grunted, and lunged, throwing my arms around his neck, wrestling the furry mass to the ground like roping a calf. In a deadlock hold, sweat trickling from my brow, I snapped on the leash. The race was on to see which one of us could make a beeline to the exit faster.

We stumbled out of the building into fresh air and bright sunshine. The invigorating scent breathed new life into my tense body as the warm sun quieted my jumbled nerves. I bent down to scratch his neck, catching a whiff of a yeasty smell. "Pee-yew. You stink." I let out a huge sigh. "Oh well. C'mon, let's get out of here."

"Where we goin'? Park?"

I led him to the car, shouting, "Yeah, yeah," relieved we had emerged unscathed. With only a twenty-five-minute drive to the house, I mused, what could possibly go wrong?

Holding his leash in one hand, I commanded him to sit in front of the tailgate. He lowered his hind quarters to the asphalt, panting intensely, as he shifted from one foot to another, eager to get moving. I unlocked the car doors and released the hatch. The back gate slowly opened. I opened the wire door to the crate and inspected the towel neatly folded on the bottom. The space appeared ready for a comfortable ride to the house. At least that's what I thought.

"Shadow, sit."

"Why?"

I reached down to pet his head. "Calm down."

"Too excited."

"Shadow, up."

He needed no further prompting to leap onto the tailgate. But instead of allowing me to guide him into his new living quarters, he nimbly bypassed the crate, jumped into the back seat, sat down, and gave me a nod with a resounding woof. I took one look at him barking, tossing his head from side to side and immediately had flashbacks of our first introduction.

"Ready to go!"

"I don't think so."

I imagined him bouncing from seat to seat like a ping pong ball, ending up on my lap while traveling down Interstate 10 at sixty-five miles an hour. No, that wasn't going to be an option. I quickly dismissed the thought of his winning this standoff. "Silly dog," I said. Who did he think he was dealing with? Then I started to wonder if this battle of wills had higher stakes than I had originally considered. If he outsmarted me, he'd be the pack leader. That wouldn't be a good thing. What? Had I lost my perspective? The thought of being bamboozled by a dog was ridiculous. I needed to get a grip quickly.

Mr. Street Smart dog, adept at the kennel game, knew all the angles to avoid being caged. To win, I would have to outmaneuver him. He evidently had practice learning how to navigate confined spaces like a hairy Houdini. So, when I tried luring him into the crate with a treat, he simultaneously caught it airborne and rocketed back out in one twist. I marveled at his athleticism. This exercise lasted several minutes until I peppered the back of the crate with a handful of treats that he couldn't snarf up before I slammed the door. Shadow barked in outrage at my victory as I closed the trunk.

"No fair."

Chugging a bottle of water to relieve my thirst only produced temporary satiation. I clutched the wheel, feeling the need to hold onto something tangible. This dog was psyching me out and we hadn't even left the parking lot. I placed the car in reverse, and looked out the back window, catching sight of his travel quarters. Shadow was safely tucked away for the ride home, but the task hadn't been easy. I managed to outwit him but wondered what would take place the next time we had a crate confrontation. *Focus, Lauren. Focus.*

That was my mantra. Now was not the time to be concerned about what might happen in the future. I had won the first round of the battle and we were heading home. That's all that mattered. Knowing that the house was only a short drive away, I slapped the steering wheel with my hand, thinking the rest of the trip would be a breeze. For ten minutes I sang along with the radio, restoring my frazzled nerves until a muted *ror-ror-ror* broke out.

"Let me out."

The eruption of barking sounded like an alarm switch had been thrown. The windows shook, making my eyes twitch as I tried to concentrate on driving.

"Shadow, no. No barking."

"Want out of this box. Now."

I was convinced we would both be deaf by the time we arrived at the house from the sound waves bouncing around the inside of the car. He drew his nails along the interior of the plastic crate in rapid succession, frantically scratching like a wild animal. I glanced in the rear-view mirror and saw a sight I had never thought possible. The gray box careened from side to side and bounced around the floor of the cargo area, looking like something out of a science fiction movie. Fearful the crate would explode, I changed my tactic and spoke in a slow, soft voice, hoping for a calming effect.

Unfortunately, the crate danced even faster. Out of solutions, I turned up the radio and hit the gas, thinking if I was pulled over for speeding, the policeman would take pity on me once he witnessed the poltergeist in the rear. There would be no detours, no stops at the pet store or the drive-through liquor store, even though the thought of drinking a frozen watermelon margarita sounded far more appealing than dealing with a frantic canine.

Twenty-five minutes seemed like a lifetime trying to manage driving, an overexcited canine in the cargo space, and non-stop barking. I let out a sigh of relief when our driveway came into view. We had both survived, but with the temperature hovering at one hundred and six degrees, we wouldn't be able to survive inside the car too long without air conditioning. I contemplated my next move.

8

THE JOY OF HOMECOMING

Every muscle in my body tensed as I tried to muster the courage to open the latch. Shadow, traumatized by the journey, stood panting, his pink tongue jetting in and out, face pressed against the wire mesh door. He coughed a couple times, making me feel even worse for the miserable ride home. The dog, both a physical and emotional mess, was all mine. An anguished sigh slipped out as the reality of the situation sunk in.

He nosed the crate door in anticipation of being released and joyfully leaped out when I opened it, pulling me to the nearest bush to pee. Afraid to let him out of my sight, I wrapped the leash around my wrist and trudged off to the garage with him in tow to collect a bucket, shampoo, three towels, and the hose, hoping the distraction would temporarily quiet my worries.

I set up a bathing area in the driveway, thinking he would put his best paw forward with Maddie if he smelled a little better. As I lathered him up with a thick coat of soap, I noticed several ticks lodged in his dense fur. I pulled the dead ones off with my fingernails, feeling squeamish as they lodged under my nail beds. The live ones, rooted into his skin on the left side of his neck, presented a much greater challenge.

Trying to remove live ticks from the soapy, slippery head of a lab moving at light speed proved to be an impossible task because, despite my determination that the ticks had to go, Shadow remained resolute that the removal of ticks was of little importance. With that, a new battle of wills erupted.

Frustrated at my continued attempts to remove the ticks, he backed up, and in one, large shake, covered me, my sunglasses, and part of the driveway in giant globs of soap suds. Following his second shake, he bolted like a horse coming out of the starting gate. Determined not to let him get away, I hung onto the leash as he raced across the concrete surface. I dug in my heels, trying to gain traction, but my old flip flops merely aided in his joy ride. He pulled me across the soapy driveway with such speed that I started to hydroplane like a water skier out for a quick spin on a lake. The aquatics show was short-lived because when I reached the edge of the driveway, I sailed into the air, landing squarely in a flower bed. Shadow stopped in his tracks. He sheepishly walked over to me and sat down.

He sported suds on his legs and torso, looking more like a poodle than a lab. I had bits of dirt and a broken flip flop remnant on my lap. I laughed until my stomach hurt.

Shadow's tail wagged and his eyes twinkled. *"Oops."*

Would Michael, Seth, or Charlie believe this story? Maybe not, but I would soon find out that the story sounded tame compared to the actual experience.

I survived, with only an unsightly bruised knee and a ruptured blood vessel in my wrist. The flowers, on the other hand, appeared permanently flattened. Shadow inspected my knee, tickling it with his wet whiskers and then bowed his head to the ground. *"Don't like baths."*

Was he giving up the fight? I had serious doubts he would surrender so easily. *Lauren, he's ready to cooperate. Better move fast.* I reached over Shadow's head and pulled all of the ticks off his neck. The seized parasites were battle trophies well worth the sacrifice. Throwing my flip flops in the garage trash can, I realized they were not a good choice of footwear when bathing Shadow.

Now it was time for him to meet Maddie. I grabbed an old pair of tennis shoes and a twenty-five-foot training lead off a shelf, said a short prayer, and released Maddie out in the front yard for a formal introduction. It was love at first sight. Within moments, they were roughhousing like two elementary school adolescents who hadn't been out for recess in a week. They charged each other, reveling in a game of chicken, colliding with such force they fell over in a heap. Standing up on their hind legs they wrestled, they were impervious to anything else happening around them, licking, pawing, and nipping. They appeared to be two old friends reuniting after a long separation. When the meet and greet was over, they were ready for the next level of integration: no leash and a large area to run in.

I led Shadow to the wooden gate accessing the backyard, leaving Maddie in the front yard. Lifting the safety latch, I pushed the door open, unsnapped the leash, and introduced him to his new playground. I left him happily sniffing his unexplored territory with the intention of retrieving Maddie from the front yard, but quickly learned that wouldn't be necessary. Muffled yips and an intermittent strike of toenails were coming from the other side of the gate. I lifted the latch and with one mighty push of Maddie's muscular neck, she barreled through the small space, sprinting toward Shadow. He bowed on all fours bracing for her attack, but Maddie bolted past him, running to the grassy area next to the pool. Shadow, in an attempt to cut her off, charged across the elevated pool deck and leaped off the edge, colliding with Maddie in mid-air. The two bodies hit the wet grass, and like race cars spinning out of control, skidded across the lawn and slammed into a pile of poop.

"Noooo!" I screamed. "Gross. Are you kidding me, I have to wash both of you?" The tick saga at this point seemed like a distant memory.

I snapped on their leashes and tied them to lounge chairs on the pool deck. I couldn't believe only one hour had elapsed since I had arrived at the house with Shadow.

My arms twitched with fatigue as I scrubbed both stinky dogs. How could I possibly survive the rest of the day, much less the evening? Charlie and Seth had soccer practice after school and

Michael had called to say he had a last-minute business dinner. This had to be the longest day of my life. And what happened to lunch?

Once again, covered in soap, dog slobber, and more hair than I had on my head, I made a vow to clean up the dog poop in the yard before letting the dogs out. I felt like a hot mess from the heat and exertion of enduring another round of baths followed by two vigorous doggie towel massages. With Shadow on my heels, I retreated to the house for a glass of water, a peanut butter chocolate chip cookie, and some air conditioning. But as I pulled the patio door open, Shadow wove his body through my legs. I tripped, falling onto the tile.

"What are you doing?"

"Same thing you're doing."

"You were in my way."

"No, you got in my way."

I stood and brushed myself off. "Well, now that we're both inside we might as well go on a house tour."

I wanted him to explore the virgin environment, but I kept him on a leash in case he decided to mark corners of furniture or the recently replaced guest bedroom carpet. Shadow lost interest in the house exploration when, through a window, he spied Maddie outside by the pool, flirting and wagging her tail, as if to say, "Come and get me."

Shadow, glaring at Maddie through the glass, thoroughly frustrated she was out of reach, reverted to a doggy solution. He charged the door, knocking his head hard against the glass. Dazed but not defeated, he whimpered, *"Yoowwie."*

Acting like a toddler throwing a temper tantrum, he dipped his head down to the floor and sprung up into the air, like Superman leaping in a single bound. With his energy welling up like a tea kettle getting ready to blow, I put the house tour on hold. Unfastening the leash was an all-star wrestling match as I pinned him to the ground long enough to coordinate the release of the clasp. Pulling the patio door open, I watched Shadow shoot out of the house like a cork from a champagne bottle. He chased Maddie for a few minutes and then broke away, running several laps around the yard to show off his impressive speed and strength.

Eventually, the two returned panting from their romp with tongues hanging out and dripping saliva on the deck. I tossed some ice cubes in their direction and filled a huge water bowl for them to share. Watching them drain the entire bowl gave me a brilliant idea. Why not cool them down with a swim? What a perfect exercise for a sizzling August day in Phoenix.

Shadow followed closely as I crossed the deck to a storage box to search for a floating dog toy. Like a child anticipating the unveiling of a wrapped birthday present, Shadow jumped onto my arms trying to catch a glimpse of what wonders awaited him in the container. Unable to fend off the rounds of pawing, I picked up a ball and in blind faith hurled it as far as I could.

The image of the dogs tearing off looked like the start of a grey-hound race. There were long, gaited strides as they raced toward the end of the property. I wasn't counting on Maddie scooping up the ball first. Shadow, outraged that he hadn't caught the prize, stayed in hot pursuit. Maddie glanced back at Shadow with gleaming eyes and then leaped into the deep end of the pool, creating a small tidal wave. Shadow, without a second thought, jumped in, too.

The impact of his plunge pushed him down underwater until he used his webbed feet to pop back to the surface. He used every ounce of energy to keep from swallowing more water. He thrashed around, pawing to stay buoyant, his wide eyes darting from side to side as his head bobbed in the waves. Water cascaded onto the deck like bursts of rain from angry thunderheads. Why wasn't he swimming to the side? Didn't Shadow know how to swim?

In disbelief, I watched the situation unfold. He tried to use his legs to elevate his body up and over the surface of the water, but no amount of kicking his back feet could accomplish that. When his head started to dip under the waves, I knew he was sinking. Panicked he would drown, I jumped in with shoes, clothes, watch, and glasses and grabbed Shadow by the collar, trying to keep a distance from his hind legs flailing under the surface. Feeling my grip, he latched onto me, clawing my shoulders and arms, sinking his back feet into my chest as leverage to stay above the surface. I could barely manage his weight and the drag of my clothes. I struggled for air, trying to shield my mouth from the splashing water. Painstakingly paddling as his clinging death grip scraped open my skin, I reached the side of the pool. Exhausted from the fight, I dipped below the surface to release his hold. He climbed over me and leaped onto the deck to get away from the water.

Shadow drew shallow pants; his wet ears flattened. *"Don't like pond."*

Hanging onto the side of the pool, I rested for a moment, unraveling twisted clothes, waiting for my adrenaline to stop thrumming. Mustering my last ounce of energy, I dragged myself out of the pool. Water gushed, splashing over my soggy sneakers. Stunned, I laid face up on the deck, sorting out the chain of events, shocked at how an innocent game of fetch had turned into a life-or-death situation. This was not how I had envisioned my first day with our new dog. I covered my eyes.

As I remained in a frozen prone position, Shadow, sensing my distress, pranced around me. *"Something wrong?"*

Both dogs barked, nudged, and licked before resorting to spraying me with whatever water was left in their thick coats. To stop their silly antics, I sat up and yelled, "We could have drowned and all you two can do is spray me with water?"

I inspected the red streaks sunk into my arms and shoulders from sharp toenails. Tank tops were not going to be a wardrobe selection for a while.

I harkened back to the six years I spent as a lifeguard, never once pulling a drowning person out of the water. Now I had undertaken one single, epic water safety act, and it was for a dog. My dog. Weren't all labs supposed to be born swimmers? That's why they have webbed paws. I made another note to myself: Next task, swimming lessons for Shadow.

I looked at my water-logged watch. What? Surely more than three hours had elapsed. Why was time still passing so slowly? I needed relief from one of my family members. Why hadn't I waited until the weekend to pick up Shadow, when Michael and the kids would have been able to help me navigate the homecoming? There was only one explanation for my decision: the fear that someone else would have adopted him. I had rushed to sign the adoption papers, spring him from the kennel, and bring him home. The thought that he could have been claimed by anyone else terrified me. I surmised my hijacked heart didn't think rationally.

When it was feeding time, I picked up their food dishes in the kitchen and retreated to the garage for dog chow. When I opened the garage door, I was surprised to see Shadow waiting for me. He dropped to the ground on all fours, barked, and shot up like a geyser exploding into the air.

"Shadow, off. Where's Maddie?"

"Dinner? Starving."

He followed me into the kitchen, continuing his joyful leaps. The smacking of lips filled the air. He ran under the table, skillfully dodging chairs. Shadow's final dance included various acrobatic stunts punctuated with barks.

"You need to wait for Maddie."

"Don't want to."

Maddie was waiting patiently by the patio door. "Time for dinner, Maddie girl." She trotted over to me as I placed the bowl on the floor. I walked over to Shadow the Cirque du Soleil performer.

"Shadow, sit."

"Why?"

"Shadow, sit."

"Sit now? Are you crazy?"

I put the bowl on the ground after he eased his butt to the floor. The hungry canines wolfed down their kibble in less than two minutes and returned to their playful activities, chasing each other around the yard.

By seven-thirty, I lost interest in watching the Labrador World Wrestling match. Needing a change of venue, I walked back to the house and started to roll the patio door open when the sound of thundering paws caught my attention. Two furry masses bounded onto the patio, neck and neck, sprinting toward me. I knew they couldn't possibly squeeze through the doorway side by side, so with both hands I grabbed the door handle and with all of my body weight swung it wide open. As the two hurled across the threshold, I hung onto the handle to prevent being swept inside by the force. A white streak headed toward the family room, followed closely by a black one. Crash!

"Maddie! Shadow!"

I regained my balance and headed into the next room. The family room lamp lay shattered around Shadow's body. Maddie, in an attempt to remove any implications of her involvement, struck the pose of an Egyptian sphinx and dodged eye contact. Shadow's ears, pasted to the back of his head, didn't flinch. The dented lamp shade, detached from the base, lay on its side.

A doggy time out was in order. I grabbed my car keys and minutes later returned to the kitchen, lugging his crate behind me.

"Shadow, come," I hollered.

His head and tail dipped to the floor as he shuffled into the kitchen.

"Shadow, into your crate," I said, throwing chicken-flavored dog treats into the back of the box.

Lowering his shoulders, looking more like a black panther than a dog, he lumbered into the crate to retrieve his treats. I slammed the door and secured the latch. Shadow pawed at the door. His mournful eyes and soft whimpers spurred a wave of guilt for putting him in the same situation he had encountered at the shelter. I knelt, placed my fingers through the mesh, and talked to him in a soothing voice.

"Everything is going to be okay, you crazy dog. But for now, I need you chill out until bedtime," I whispered softly. "I have two things to take care of right now. Well, maybe I'll leave the mess in the family room for someone else to clean up later. The one job I have to do before letting you two outside again is to make a poop inspection." My voice trailed off as I approached the door. "I'll be right back." I retreated to the side yard to pick up a shovel but realized it was too dark to see anything. Walking back to the house to get a flashlight, I heard muffled barking. Craning my neck forward, I gawked at a black furry figure bouncing around like a kangaroo in front of the patio door. Paws were thumping the glass door with such force I hoped it wouldn't shatter into a million pieces. Rushing toward the house I shouted, "No, Shadow. What are you doing?"

I grabbed the door handle and pushed it open. Shadow leaped forward, pouncing on my chest several times as if to scold me for leaving him in the crate. Yanking him off me, I walked back inside the house and ventured over to the scene of the crime. As I suspected, the face of the crate looked oddly mangled. The door hinge rested crookedly against the tile floor and the wire mesh had popped out. I looked at Shadow, then looked back at the demolished crate. "I don't know how you did that, but thank God you're okay. You could have really hurt yourself." I reached out, petting him nervously, making rapid strokes down his back.

"Don't like those crate things."

"Oh, no. Now what am I going to do? I don't have another crate." Shadow licked his lips. "I wonder if I should call Michael and ask him to pick one up on his way home. Shoot, can't do that——he's at dinner."

Centered on all fours, Shadow barked, each woof louder than the last. *"Bad idea."*

How could I keep him confined for the night? Visions of him peeing on the carpet, chewing on shoes, or worse, destroying a cell phone casually left on a counter, provoked a wave of uneasiness. How would I be able to sleep if I needed one eye open all the time? Before I had time to think about a solution, Charlie and Seth bounded in through the garage door.

"Where's our new pup..." But before Seth finished the word, Shadow was at his feet, barking loud enough to be heard in the next county. He jumped on Seth and licked his hands. *"Who are you?"*

"He's a puppy? I thought he was an elephant," Seth asked, taking a step back.

"Yes, I'm afraid he's a little wound up right now. Don't worry, he'll settle down."

"You smell okay." Shadow waved his nose in the air at Seth and then circled Charlie. *"You smell okay, too."*

Charlie piped up. "Wow, he's gorgeous. I want to play with him, but I'm starving. What's for dinner?"

"I didn't have time to make dinner. It's been a ridiculous day bringing Shadow home. There are a few leftovers in the fridge, but if you don't want that, you can order pizza. Dad's out for dinner with clients, so just order for yourselves. After you get cleaned up, maybe you could spend some time with Shadow——that would give me time to make a salad."

"Okay, I'm going to shower and then rummage through the fridge," Charlie said as he walked away. "Mom! What happened in the family room? It's a disaster."

I sighed. "Well, the dogs went a little crazy chasing each other through the house and by the time I caught up with them the damage was already done. I could use some help on clean-up detail."

"Of course! But you seem pretty calm about it. Aren't you mad about the broken lamp?" Charlie asked.

"I don't have enough energy to be mad. This has just been an insane day. I'm trying to manage one minute at a time. Seriously, these two pooches remind me of how you two used to run me ragged when you were toddlers. Together, they're a train wreck."

Charlie smiled.

"Shadow's beautiful," Seth said as he skimmed the dog's trunk. "Now we have two labs, huh?"

"Are you trying to make sure I won't return Shadow to the rescue tomorrow?"

"You wouldn't do that, would you? I want another dog."

"I can tell you that Shadow makes me feel like we have ten dogs, not two."

After showering, both boys got to work cleaning up the family room while I ordered pizza and made a salad. I guess they really wanted another dog.

The boys devoured dinner in record time. Clean-up was easy because there weren't any leftovers. As I wiped down the kitchen counters, I turned and saw Shadow standing on his hind legs, paws gripping the edge of the dining room table, his tongue making wide sweeps on the surface.

"Shadow, off!" I yelled.

"Pizza, yum."

"Bad dog," I said, spraying the table with bleach water.

"Just helping you clean up."

"Do we need to practice the "off" command?"

"Nope, already know that one, too."

"C'mon, trouble, time to chill out on the couch and wait for Dad to come home." My intention was to give Michael a formal introduction to Shadow, but I dozed off. When Shadow heard the garage door open, he let out a stream of barks that sounded like five smoke detectors all going off at the same time. Startled, I blurted out, "Aaaah, Shadow, you scared me to death. Stop barking." I grabbed his collar and yanked him toward me. "Sit, Shadow. It's just Michael, he's part of our family, too. Calm down."

"Doing my job." Shadow sat on his haunches.

Michael walked into the family room, not knowing what to expect amidst the booms of barking. Shadow ran over to him and inhaled deeply.

"Same smell, you must be part of the pack." Shadow jumped up on his hind legs and threw his paws onto Michael's chest.

"Shadow, down."

"Just wanted a closer look."

Michael put his hand out for Shadow to sniff. "So, this is Shadow. He's very handsome, but is he always this excitable?"

"Yup."

"No. Well, yes, I mean, maybe a little——I don't know. Remember, I only spent a couple of hours walking him while I was at the kennel."

"Kennel! Those things make me nervous."

"I can tell he has quite the personality. But the barking..."

"Sorry, hon, what did you say?"

Michael looked at Shadow. "Would you stop barking?"

"Can't. Too excited."

"Sorry, I didn't hear you. Did you say he's endearing?"

"Not exactly, but..."

"Oh hon, just give it time," I shouted over the woofing. "Shadow! Sit."

Shadow rolled his ears back and sat down in front of Michael. *"Sorry."* He lowered his gaze and extended a paw to softly brush Michael's knee.

Michael reached down to pet Shadow on the head. "That's a good dog."

"Awe. I can tell he's already charming the socks off you. Welcome to the Shadow Pushover Club." I paused for a second. "You know he does seem a little over the top tonight. Good thing I have a couple days off from work. I don't think I could leave Shadow at the house unsupervised. He's a little crazy right now, but I'm sure he'll settle right in by the weekend."

"That was good thinking on your part, but I think you're going to need more than a few days."

"No worries. I've got this." *Why did I just say that? After everything that happened today. I need another reality check.*

As we retreated for the bedroom, I told Michael about the day's activities and the crate incident, all of which had rendered me exhausted. I threw a mass of towels on the floor beside our bed and commanded Shadow to lie down.

Too tired to follow the nightly get-ready-for-bed ritual, I flopped on the bed and waited for sleep to erase the nightmares of the day. Shadow must have been completely worn out, too, because only an occasional snort could be heard before he drifted off to a deep sleep. Sometime in the middle of the night, the weight from his warm paws gently resting on the edge of the bed jerked me awake. A tender flick of his tongue on my cheek followed.

"I'm worried about crates and that pond."

Sleepily, I reached out and stroked his head until he buried his muzzle into the crook of my neck. When his wiry whiskers tickled my chin, I gently lifted his muzzle and placed it on the edge of the bed. "Shadow, go back to your bed."

He slowly slunk away. The click of toenails stopped when he reached the towels. Why had he awoken me? For reassurance, attention? I didn't want to think about it. He had gone back to sleep, and that was all that mattered. He had been a challenge during the day but at least I didn't have to worry about him sleeping at night.

9

HOUDINI IN THE KITCHEN

The next morning, I staggered out of bed hoping yesterday's chain of events wouldn't be repeated. Michael had already left to go to the office for an early morning meeting, so I was left to fend off Shadow's pleas for breakfast. The whirling dervish rebounded off the floor and kitchen counter, and then slammed into my chest, pushing me backwards. "Shadow, stop," I said grabbing his paws, pushing them to the floor.

"You're acting like a pinball in an arcade game."

"Starving."

Charlie and Seth, witnessing my distraction with Shadow, snagged power bars and mumbled something about stopping for food on their way to school as they rushed out the door. I relaxed my shoulders. *Stay calm. He's hungry. Nothing a regular feeding schedule won't fix. Lauren, don't get all wigged out about it.*

Retreating to the garage to fill the dogs' food bowls with kibble, I spied the mangled crate, ready for trash pick-up. Patti's advice to keep Shadow in a kennel at night and when left alone in the house echoed in my ears like a song on repeat. But how could I shop for a new crate without leaving him unsupervised? My throat burned. Heartburn so early in the morning was not a good omen.

Without crating him, I knew the chances of finding the house still intact on my return were greatly reduced. The idea of being held prisoner in my house by a high-spirited lab because he couldn't be crated was absurd. I considered calling Patti for advice but decided I didn't want to bother her. Out of ideas, I made a desperate call to my canine-loving neighbor, Cynthia, and asked if she could dog sit while I ran to the store. Thankfully, she sensed the urgency in my voice and came right over. After briefly introducing her to Shadow, I set out on my shopping expedition.

Going from one pet store to another was like a scavenger hunt, but after perusing three stores, I found a kennel that looked more like a hotel than a cage. The solid steel wire frame was enormous and sturdy enough for a hundred-twenty-five-pound dog. With Shadow weighing in at a mere seventy pounds there would be ample room for him to move around.

When I opened the door leading from the garage to the house, Shadow leaped in celebration of my return until spying his new quarters being wheeled in on a dolly. As I pushed the crate into the family room, Shadow stared at me.

"Another one?"

"Hi, Cynthia. Thanks for covering for me. I appreciate you doing this so much. Hope Shadow behaved for you."

"Oh, no worries, glad I could help," she replied cheerfully. "The dogs were well behaved, but you do have your hands full. I think Shadow missed you while you were gone. He parked himself on the sofa and looked out the window. Wow, that's an enormous crate."

"Yeah." I hesitated, not wanting to explain what had happened to the last one. "I'm going to make a batch of chocolate chip toffee scones as a thank you——I'll drop them off in say, maybe a week? We're still trying to settle in with our new addition. I haven't had time to cook much of anything in the last twenty-four hours."

"You don't have to do that, but I know the kids will be thrilled," she said as she headed out the door. "Call me anytime."

I pulled the crate off the dolly and placed a soft blanket inside the doggie hotel with his favorite treats, leaving the door open for him to inspect the space without fear of entrapment. I crawled inside several times to demonstrate how comfortable the space could be. One time, he accompanied me and although it was a bit crowded, all body parts fit except my legs. The situation became more complicated when we both tried to exit at the same time.

"Shadow! Would you wait a second until I get my head out?"

"Why do you always get to go first?"

I knew getting Shadow to relax in a crate would be a challenge, but I thought I'd be able to solve the problem if I applied the basic principles of behavior modification I studied in child psychology classes. They worked well on Seth and Charlie, why wouldn't the method work on Shadow? I had already made the crate comfortable and enticed him to enter the space by placing a treat at the back of the cage, so the next step was to start the desensitizing process. I gave Shadow the command to go into the crate, stay and lay down. Every time he went in and stayed calm, I rewarded him with more food and praise. He knew the drill but was nonetheless conflicted. Entering the crate would afford him a mass of tasty chicken treats, but he would have to sacrifice his independence for time behind bars. His stomach won the argument and he reluctantly stepped into the kennel with my command. My five-pound stash of treats was being depleted rapidly. Good thing he never tired of chicken. Over the next hour I extended the sessions from five minutes, to ten, to fifteen.

"Wahoo, Shadow. You've got this crate thing down, right?"

"Wrong."

That answer would have been easy to figure out if I had paid attention to his rigid body language after his fifteen-minute session. The only other time he sat quietly looking like a statue cast in stone was the first day we met, just seconds before his Tasmanian performance. Why didn't I remember that?

I decided to test whether the behavior modification technique had worked. With no fanfare, I made out a shopping list, exited the house and headed for the car. I stopped abruptly, wondering if a trip to the grocery store for dinner items was a good idea. The last time I crated him ended up being a disaster. What if the same thing happened? *Do the responsible thing, Lauren. Grocery shopping can wait.*

I scrambled around to the side yard, sat on a pile of bricks, and waited anxiously for ten minutes. Ten minutes is a really long time when waiting for something you hope will not happen, like when you get stopped by police and you sit for what seems to be an eternity before finding out whether you're going to get a ticket.

Glancing at my watch, I decided I couldn't wait any longer. I hurried around the corner of the house, and there, in clear view, a black figure bounced up and down in front of the patio door. A thick wad of white saliva slid down the window. Muffled barking and whining projected through the glass along with the rhythmic tail that slapped the door frame. I jumped to unlatch the door. "Shadow! Who are you, Houdini reincarnated as a dog?"

"Look! I got out of the crate."

I peeled back the door. "Sit, Shadow."

"Can't sit, too excited." He hurled his paws at my chest knocking us both to the ground. Pleased with the success of initiating such a warm welcome, he compulsively licked my face.

How did he escape? And did he suffer any injuries trying to break free?

"Ta-da! Did it again."

I tried to sit up, but he pinned me down, finding comfort in covering any exposed flesh with repeated slurps. I untangled myself so I could examine his body for signs of missing fur, blood, or other injuries. My curiosity piqued as I inspected the wire-meshed bars for clues to his escape. One of the side panels was slightly bowed, allowing him to squeeze out of the narrow space where the front and side panels were wired together. How he had managed to wiggle his body through that tiny space and not suffer puncture wounds would have to remain a mystery.

He was amped up from his jail break for the remainder of the day. Jittery and excitable, he wandered around with his head down and avoided eye contact, swinging his lean frame from side to side. Obsessively walking as if on a tight rope, he would pace to the end of the kitchen, abruptly turn on his heels, and head back. He looked like a caged tiger pacing back and forth. Any effort to temporarily break his stride proved futile because as soon as I stopped petting him, he'd fall back into pacing. He was in a trance. Whenever he stopped for a few seconds, a mass of white slobber from his muzzle slid to the floor in frothy puddles. The sound of his rhythmic panting paused only when he was face down in the water dish. He slurped so much that I padded the floor with thick towels anticipating the next release of water carried in his jowls.

I felt helpless, filling his water dish too many times to count. His swollen belly, the result of his unquenchable thirst and endless panting, looked like he had swallowed a basketball. Was this string of repeated behaviors the only way he knew how to quiet his fears and ease nervousness? I needed to switch things up and snap him out of whatever he was obsessing about. Removing the crate from the house had to help. I lugged the wire box to the car for the return to the store. There would be no more crates for Shadow.

But now I had a new challenge. If Shadow couldn't be crated, how would I keep an eleven-month-old troublemaker, who thought he was Houdini, in the house? I had no idea how to solve that issue, but I had to manage one crisis at a time. Rummaging through the freezer for dinner options, there was a flank steak I could thaw for tomorrow night's dinner. But without a trip to the grocery store, the menu choices for the evening's meal were limited. I decided to serve cheesy scrambled eggs, jalapeno-praline bacon, sliced strawberries, and sour-dough toast. Fortunately, there were no protests.

Later that evening, resting for a brief moment with my feet up on the couch, I laughed at how quickly I had begun referring to Shadow as Houdini dog. He was a mystery on many levels.

Shadow was the name the shelter found on his scanned registra-tion chip. The microchip, implanted under his skin, also identified the name and address of his owners. After they were contacted twice and declined to take their dog back, he was officially homeless. I couldn't figure out why the previous owners gave him that name. "Shadow" didn't seem to reflect his personality. To me, the name Shadow had a gloomy connotation. There wasn't a low-spirited bone in his body. I thought about how shadows cast dark shapes by blocking light. He didn't block light, he reflected it. When the sun hit his ink-black coat, sunglasses were required to look at him. I observed him as I said out loud, "Shadow. Shadow." More possibilities rolled through my head, but obvious names such as Pepper, Dracula, or Cinder didn't seem to capture his persona, either.

Michael walked into the family room and joined me on the couch. "I heard you repeating Shadow's name. Is he up to something again?"

"No, but I've been thinking we should change his name. I don't like it. Shadow doesn't capture his spirit. What do you think?"

"It seems like an ordinary name. Let's face it, so far he's turned out to be anything but ordinary," Michael laughed.

I shared the names I had considered, and Michael agreed they were too pedestrian.

"What do you think of Magic? Kinda fits. You know, as in black magic? There might have been supernatural forces at work when he escaped from two crates in two days. And, I'm still not convinced that he didn't put a spell on you the first time you met."

"Funny," I said. I thought a little longer. "So, you think Magic is the right name for him?" I asked, giving Michael a quizzical look. "I can't put my finger on exactly why I'm agreeing with you, but the name does seem to fit. He has proven to be sort of a wonder dog so far." I slowly nodded my head. "Yes, you're right. We'll call him Magic."

10

OUR NAVY SEAL

Only one day had passed since my gallant effort to save Magic from drowning. One day? Seemed more like a month. The thought of yesterday's swimming saga was unnerving. The reality that we had an unfenced pool weighed heavily on my mind all night. If Magic mistakenly fell in, the outcome could be fatal. I needed to plunge in head-first with swimming lessons. I bit my lip, trying to manage anxious thoughts about handling a mass of thrashing torso and legs in four feet of water.

The next morning, I changed into a swimsuit, slipped on a long sleeve t-shirt for extra protection from jabbing toenails, grabbed his leash, and casually walked him out to the pool area. I didn't want Magic to pick up on my nervous vibe, so I started singing the Bee Gee's song, "Stayin' Alive." He followed me to the pool steps and watched with great interest as I slipped into waist-deep water.

"Magic, come," I said firmly.

"Don't like the pond."

Instead of coming to me, he dropped his ears, backed away, and sat down. I had déjà vu, recalling the circumstances of our standoff with the crate game. I exited the pool, picked up the leash, and skimmed my hand down his neck. His fur felt like a hot bed of coals. When he heard the click of the lead, he threw his muzzle into the air, straining his neck to the side and refusing to go near the water. There was only one solution: pick him up and carry him into the water.

"Okay, here we go," I said, gathering up the leash in one hand. He didn't seem remotely interested in what I had planned for the afternoon's activity. As I reached down to scoop him into my arms, he panicked. His eyes bulged like a frog. Sticky foam from his muzzle smeared my shirt. His weight was as unwieldly as a burlap sack of potatoes. I struggled to juggle his every move and maintain my balance as I lurched down the steps. I wedged my neck across his back like a vise to keep him in place. There was only one thing Magic wanted to do——get out of the pool. His legs, beating like a stand mixer whipping cream, sprayed sheets of water into the air.

I was thankful we were in the shallow end. As I shifted my hands to place one under his belly and the other in front of his chest, I talked to him calmly, trying to reassure him that he would survive. But he wasn't interested in my tranquil rhetoric. He wiggled his torso and thrashed his legs, shooting water in all directions, including up my nose, triggering a sneezing fit. Magic didn't appreciate the fact that his personal flotation device was not paying attention to the crisis at hand. He wiggled out of my arms, positioned his legs against my thighs and pushed off. He rebounded right at me, his full body weight hitting me in the chest. As I staggered backwards, his front legs flew over my shoulders, pushing me to the bottom of the pool. I looked up and saw Magic frantically paddling in circles as if he was auditioning for a synchronized swim team. When I surfaced, he pawed me and thrust his jaw forward like a snapping turtle, his white teeth inches from my swim skirt. I dove for the steps. He paddled fiercely to get to the steps, too. When he reached them, he pushed off his hind legs, hopped out of the water, and shook out his coat more efficiently than the spin cycle of a washing machine. Magic trotted to the grass and sat down, anchoring his butt firmly to the ground.

"Go ahead. Try to get me into the pond."

I climbed out of the pool, marched across the lawn and grabbed the water-soaked leash in one hand. "Magic, come," I commanded, dragging him toward the pool steps. Looking at his flattened ears and tucked tail I felt guilty for strong-arming him into the pool.

"C'mon, boy. You can do this," I said confidently.

He resisted for a moment, then walked down two steps.

"Good dog," I said excitedly.

Magic leaped from the second step out onto the deck. *"Told you, don't like the pond."*

He stood glistening in the sun with no sign of wanting anything to do with water other than drink it from a bowl. I knew another battle of wills was about to unfold.

I ignored him, climbed out of the pool and walked to the source of yesterday's disaster: the toy box. Lifting the lid and plucking out a tennis ball, I said enticingly, "Look what I have."

Magic's ear pricked forward.

"Do you want it?" I asked, parading by him and tossing the toy into the air.

Magic's head bobbed up and down, tracking the ball. With a lifted tail and fiery eyes dancing in the sunlight, he followed me to the edge of the pool. Watching me slowly walk backward down the pool steps, he pawed the deck and bounced into the air, barking in defiance. *"Want it, now."*

He reluctantly put his paws in the water and crept down onto the first step. Holding the ball over my head in one hand, I reached in for the leash with the other, and with one final pull, he plunged into the water, following me around the shallow end in hot pursuit of the toy.

"Wahoo!"

As he paddled, he gained confidence. Graceful would not be an accurate description of his swimming style because he worked so hard to stay afloat. He had his own technique, but I wasn't critical, having accomplished my objective of keeping him from drowning. Magic had mastered the official dog paddle, earning the title of Navy Seal dog.

After resting for a few minutes, I introduced a game of pool fetch to acknowledge his new-found skill and give him a bit more practice. I let Maddie out of the house, and both dogs raced into the water to be the first one to retrieve the tennis ball. After what seemed like thirty rounds of the game, Magic retreated to the sunniest part of the pool area, circled twice, and eased his tired body down onto the deck. Maddie joined him. He looked comfortable resting on his side, so I headed to the kitchen to prep dinner. I marinated the flank steak, whipped up an Asian barbecue sauce and cleaned the broccoli and mushrooms. With the steak and mushrooms ready for the grill, the only remaining task was to steam the broccoli, which I could do while the steak was cooking. Dinner would be ready in a flash when everyone came home.

Looking at my watch, I saw that twenty minutes had elapsed. I grabbed a glass of water, wandered over to the patio door, and peered out to check on Magic. There he was, on his back, legs twitching, all four paws making wild jabs in the air, dreaming like only dogs do. Was he chasing a squirrel or fighting off an intruder?

A tremor must have jolted him awake. He lifted his head, yawned, and then rolled over on all fours, surveying the pool. His head swiveled right, left, right, and stopped. He extended his neck, his ears flicking forward and back as he stared intently at the water. I noticed his hackles standing straight up and loose flaps of skin tightening around his muzzle. Scrambling to an upright position, he turned away from the pool, sprinted to a dense row of hedges, leaned in, and peed. Distancing himself from the saturated foliage, he lowered his head to the base of the shrubs and forced it through the branches. As he poked through, a couple of small sticks rolled off his nose. His face, framed by green leaves, resembled a Chia Pet. I laughed from my vantage point inside. What was he doing?

As he tried to dip his nose toward the ground, foliage from the branches rained on his snout. He pulled out of the bush and sprinted to a red hibiscus plant near the water's edge. Although still partially camouflaged, I could see his muscles rippling as the sun shined on his coat. He side-stepped one of the branches and lowered his tummy to the ground, like a sailor dropping to crab crawl. What was he up to? Maddie was sound asleep, there weren't any ducks paddling around, and no toys were in sight, just a chlorinator moving gently along the surface of the water. Surely, he wasn't interested in a piece of pool equipment. Silly dog.

The chlorinator, short and squat in shape, looked like a giant mushroom with a blue top and white body. The kids had nick-named it Blue. Not very creative, I'm afraid.

Magic, still looking at the chlorinator, stood frozen for a couple minutes, like an ice statue. The only movement was when his chest expanded slightly when he drew a breath. He stretched out a paw to the deck and nervously glanced to both sides, a sniper observing the enemy. Did he think he was being watched? Dinner would have to wait. I had a real-life drama unfolding in my back yard. Stepping quietly outside, I crouched down behind a palm tree to set up surveillance.

Magic shifted his weight from his back feet to a forward stance, making him look tall and fit. The tip of his tail quivered and his ears popped up to capture any sounds. He was ready for action, our Navy Seal minus the flippers.

He crab-crawled across the deck. Then, our Seal slithered down the steps and entered the water, slowly, his body bobbing effortlessly. His snout and head skimmed the surface like a crocodile seeking out prey. I watched with interest. No, he couldn't be thinking Blue, the chlorinator, was a toy?

I didn't like where this scenario was headed. He paddled in wide loops around the blue mushroom with calculated efficiency, like he was doing reconnaissance. He drew tighter and tighter circles, his eyes fixated, watching Blue dance with the waves.

He was getting ready to attack.

"No, Magic, no!" I yelled. "Not the chlorinator." My plea fell on deaf ears. He made his move, and with one swift underwater pull of his legs, he lunged, striking the target with his paws. He attacked from different directions. Blue took multiple hits. Based on his reaction, it was clear that he didn't just want to incapacitate Blue, he wanted the thing obliterated. Did he think the chlorinator was a weapon of mass destruction? Frustrated that his tactics were not working, Navy Seal guided the chlorinator with his nose to the shallow end until he reached the steps.

I bolted from my hiding place onto the deck and tripped over the leg of the chaise lounge, belly flopping onto the chair. Magic, focused on the chlorinator wedged between his chest and the side of the pool, didn't look up. With a better hold, he leaned in for a bite. The outside plastic collar peeled off. Satisfied he had disarmed it, the search for the possible embedded ammunition began as he attempted to pry off the lid. He dragged Blue out of the pool and dropped it on the deck. Pieces of white plastic speckled the area, but the top was still secure.

Speechless, I stared in disbelief.

"Almost done."

In frustration, Navy Seal barked. The lid would simply not budge. But he was a dog on a mission. I didn't know whether to laugh or scream as I watched him throw his head around, wet fur shining like an oil slick, body leaping into the air like a bucking horse. With renewed spirit, he bent down and clasped the side of Blue with his teeth. Then, with a head snap, he flung it feet into the air. Navy Seal was a one-dog wrecking crew. Fragments of plastic littered the deck. The top popped off and the partially dissolved chlorine tablets exploded into the air, looking like bars of soap. Magic sat on his haunches and gave out a long bark. He seemed pleased that he had fought a noble battle and emerged the victor.

"Pond safe now."

I inspected my body for injuries from the chaise lounge landing and scooted down to the end of the chair. I glared at Magic. What the heck was up with this dog? He had learned to swim and take out the chlorinator all in one day?

"Ahhhh! You're a train wreck. That's not a good boy. Look at this mess." I gave him my best stink eye. "Something new to clean up. What a shock."

After sweeping up the debris and toweling off Navy Seal, I brought him inside. He trotted to the pantry door and sat down.

"Mission complete. How about a treat?"

"You're looking for a treat? Treats are for good doggies. I don't think you were a good doggie, but I know you're hungry from all that swimming." I tossed him a couple chicken jerky strips that he plucked out of the air. "And now I have to run to the store and buy a new chlorinator." I glared at Magic. "Poor Blue." Magic looked away.

I grabbed my purse and car keys, headed for the garage, and stopped. *Lauren, get with the program. Leaving Magic alone in the house, uncrated? Not a good idea. But I have to replace the chlorine dispenser right away. Hmmm. I know, I'll take him to the pool store with me. That will solve both probl...nope, bad idea.* I envisioned him pulling every pool toy in reach off the store shelves. I picked up the phone. "Hi, Cynthia, me again. I was wondering if you could stay with Magic and Maddie while I go to the store?"

"I thought his name was Shadow?"

"Well, it was, but we renamed him yesterday."

"I thought you just got him yesterday."

"We did, but we thought we should change his name right away because we didn't like Shadow. And speaking of him, he tore up our chlorinator for the pool. I need to go out and buy a new one."

"No problem. Give me ten minutes."

"Thanks."

I barely said hello to Cynthia before racing out the door.

Arriving at the pool store in record time, I jogged to the back of the building and spoke to Mark, a young store clerk with a headband around his curly blonde hair, about what had happened. He thought the story was hilarious, amused by my tale of woe. A bucket of tabs and the new unit cost me over fifty dollars. As I reached the exit of the store, I heard Mark talking to another employee, "Oh, she'll be back for another one. Soon."

I hustled back to the house to relieve Cynthia of her duties, promising that in addition to the scones I would also bake three dozen chewy chocolate cherry chunk cookies for her family.

After filling Blue II with chlorine tabs and releasing it into the shallow end, I heard a muted bark from inside the house. I turned to see Magic watching intently.

"Another one. Navy Seal, ready."

I slowly opened the door. Magic came bounding out.

"Magic, sit. Listen to me, doggy-doggy. See that thing floating out there?" I pointed with my finger. "That is not your new play toy. We need chlorine in the pool so don't even think about going after that. Don't make me put you in time out." Hmmm. Sounded like a great idea except that I didn't have a way to do that. Where would I put him for a time out?

He sat quietly, looking at the chlorinator then at me. With squinty eyes and perked up ears, he barked. *"Navy Seal called to action."*

"Don't bark at me. You're making me crazy. Leave it alone, you hear me?" Magic cocked his head with each inflection of my voice, listening intently to every word. "I said leave-it-alone! These things are expensive. I'm not interested in buying another one. Can't you just swim around like a regular dog? Oh yeah, you're not a regular dog. How could I forget that?"

I headed toward the patio door believing he would heed the stern warning. Ten seconds later I heard a splash. Navy Seal had taken a calculated plunge from the side of the pool and landed dead center on top of Blue II.

I screamed, "Hey, did you hear anything I just said?"

Too late. When the tank popped out from under his tummy, he grabbed it with his teeth, pinned it to the side of the pool, and ripped off the collar, just like he did with Blue.

"You have to be kidding me. Did you really just do that?" Shouting only made him lash out at the chlorinator with more determined attacks.

By the time I was able to recapture it from him, the dome was in pieces. "Bad dog," I belted out, ripping the mangled mess out of his hold. "Great, now I have to buy another one."

"Mission complete."

I put my hands on my hips and scolded Magic, "Do you think you can bark any louder?" I walked over to the lounge chair and picked up my cell phone. "Why don't you keep barking while I'm talking to Cynthia? That way she'll know what a nut case I'm dealing with."

"Can't help it, excited."

"Hi, Cynthia." I paused not wanting to say why I was calling again. "Could you watch Magic again one more time? I'm sorry for asking. He just demolished the new chlorinator. I'm worried about algae…"

"Sure, no problem."

I promised a dinner for her family and drove back to the pool store.

"Hi Mark. I'm sure you remember me. I'm back to buy another chlorinator."

"Oh, yes, hi. We do sell a lot of chlorinators to dog owners. I bet I can guess the breed."

"I bet you can, too. But spare me. I have two labs that might be in their puppy stage forever. I know one of them gets bored around the pool when there aren't any toys available, but the way he killed the chlorinator you'd think he's on some kind of seek-and-destroy mission. You know, working undercover. A Navy Seal, only he's got black fur. Get it, black sea lion…black lab?" I laughed at my own joke when Mark didn't. "But seriously, do you have a comparable product that's indestructible?"

"No. Just the ones you see on the shelf."

"I would pay large sums of money to know I wouldn't have to be returning for another one. I can't believe somebody hasn't made a dog-proof chlorinator. It would be a best seller. Any ideas on what I could do?"

"Ummm, no."

"I'm going to figure something out. This is the last time I'm paying for one of these things." I walked over to the shelf, grabbed the tank, marched over to the cash register, and handed Mark my credit card.

"Thanks." I lifted the bag off the counter and left in a huff. Navy Seal was not going to win this battle.

I made a quick detour to a hardware store to purchase a small piece of chicken wire and a roll of string in preparation for crafting the ultimate chew-proof tank.

When I returned home, I thanked Cynthia for keeping the dogs company, adding the delivery of the food might be a few weeks out.

At the rate I was calling her for help, I was on track to becoming her personal chef.

I spent the next two hours in the comfort of my air-conditioned kitchen molding the wire into a square mesh cage that had a hinged lid for easy access to the chlorinator. Thinking my design was ingenious, I considered the idea of submitting a patent but wondered when I would ever have time to do that. The finished product resembled the small, wire-mesh pots my father and I used years ago when we went crabbing.

Magic nudged my arm several times. *"What's that?"*

"Stop pestering me. And no, this is not for you."

"Navy Seal on standby."

I exited the house, filled the top chamber of the chlorinator with chlorine tabs, screwed the plastic lid tight, and lowered Blue III into the wire cage. I tied the hinged door closed with a long piece of string and set the new contraption afloat. In honor of the newly enhanced version of Blue, I decided to change the name to Stealth, feeling confident the design could survive any future attacks. The mesh cage bobbed serenely along the surface, with Stealth tucked safely inside. I let Navy Seal out of the house. He wasted no time slipping out the door, taking cover behind a bush, and waiting for an opportune moment to strike.

As Stealth floated into his peripheral view, Navy Seal seized the moment. He jumped in and landed within a foot of the cage. He thrust his front paws forward, hitting Stealth from every direction. To his frustration, the assault didn't work, so he scrambled his whole body over the top of the chlorinator, pushing the cage below the surface. Magic frantically tried to keep Stealth submerged, but it slipped out from under his belly, catapulting a foot into the air and crash landing on Magic's head.

"RRRrrrr-yowwww. Ouch."

"I think you better leave Stealth alone. It's over."

"Watch this."

Navy Seal wrestled with the cage, pinning it to the side of the pool. He threw his flank into the mesh, slightly denting one side. He tried pulling the mangled box up the steps and onto the deck but stopped when he couldn't figure out a way to grab the mesh with his teeth. Exhausted from bombarding Stealth, he let the cage float away into the deep end.

Navy Seal vaulted up the steps out of the pool and shook vigorously. Dropping to a crouched position, with his head low and ears forward, he continued to focus on the evil chlorinator. Suddenly, in another giant leap, Magic splashed close to the cage, but instead of storming the tank, he grabbed the excess string hanging over one side in his mouth and began swimming, pulling Stealth around the perimeter of the pool.

"Navy Seal wins."

Stealth enjoyed the ride as Magic proudly dispensed chlorine throughout the pool. That is how Navy Seal and Stealth became good buddies that summer.

"Good job!"

If you can't beat them, join them. I felt relieved the pool drama had closure.

11

THE DOG CATCHER IN THE CLOSET

I had no idea that when I adopted Magic, he would wreak havoc during the day and mayhem at night for days——and nights——on end. The only experience I could compare it to was bringing our newborns home from the hospital. There was pooping, peeing, sleep deprivation, and need for attention——only this time I was living in a universe driven by an eleven-month-old lab. I marginally survived the first day Magic came to live with us. There was the harrowing transport to our house, the near drowning dog incident, the Houdini crate escape, and the Tasmanian Devil bathing episode, all of which had left me deliriously tired by eight o'clock that evening, ready to fall into bed. Fortunately, Magic was spent that night, too, waking me up only once with a kiss.

The second day of activities had included another Houdini escape, swimming lessons, a game of fetch, and a Navy Seal mission. I assumed all these events would have a similar effect on his readiness to crash for the night. I learned the hard way that assuming what my rescue dog might or might not do could come back to bite me.

That night, Charlie and Seth finished their homework and said good night to Michael and me as we hung out in the family room. Maddie, tuckered out from Magic's introduction to the household and their pool activities, lay curled in a tight ball at the foot of the couch. Her legs twitched and her paws jerked back and forth, making a clicking sound as they raked across the tile. Magic, busy inspecting under the table for any morsels left over from dinner, sprinted periodically from one end of the table to the other for no apparent reason, looking bright-eyed and ready for the next family activity.

I looked over at Michael. "Honey, I'm going to take the dogs outside to pee and then fall into bed. I'm beat. It's been another long day."

"I know, and I'm sorry for all he's put you through today, but I'm watching him making donuts around the dinner table. There's nothing about him that screams tired to me. He seems kind of antsy." Michael paused. "Too bad we can't crate him. I know we already tried that." We rolled our eyes. "I'm almost afraid to ask——where is he going to sleep tonight?"

"In our room?" I said sheepishly. "I need to keep an eye on him; otherwise, who knows what he'll get into."

Michael shook his head. "I didn't see the crazy stunts he pulled earlier, but now he's acting like he drank a quart of coffee instead of water. He's going to be up all night. I'm telling you. He has issues."

"Sheesh, remember when Seth kept us up at night for weeks and we suffered from sleep deprivation?" I reminded him, only half-jokingly.

"I didn't like it back then and——"

"Ohhh, c'mon, surely you don't think Magic is going to be that big a problem. I know he has boundless puppy-like energy and requires a lot of attention right now, but he's going to be fine. Today he learned to swim, and chased Maddie in the yard for at least ten miles." I winked at Michael. "The other activities I would rather not mention on grounds of avoiding self-incrimination."

"Okay, but I have to work tomorrow, and I don't want my sleep interrupted in the middle of the night," he responded. "And on that note, I'm going to bed. Maybe if I fall asleep first it will help. Give me fifteen minutes to get settled. I'll see you in the morning."

I scowled at Michael's back and then turned to open the patio door, calling Magic and Maddie to the backyard for one last bathroom visit. Having drunk two bowls of water, Magic seemed grateful to find a bush close to the house. Maddie bounded back inside looking for a treat. She gulped down a tasty wafer I chucked in her direction and then bee-lined to her bed, circling three times before dropping gracefully.

"Good night, Maddie," I said sweetly, turning off the kitchen lights.

Magic followed on my heels into the bedroom as if worried that even a brief lag in his step might suggest he would sleep in the kitchen, too. I turned and looked into his wide eyes. "Don't worry, Magic," I said in a hushed voice. "I won't banish you to the kitchen, but I do need to figure out where and what your bed is going to be. Hmmm... let's see what's in the linen closet that might be more suitable than the mishmash of towels I used last night."

Improvising with an assortment of blankets and sheets, I assembled a comfortable nest near the head of our bed. Magic, unimpressed with the neatly swirled linens, took one look, leaped onto the bed and flopped down on his huge haunches in the middle of the mattress, bumping his bear-sized paws carelessly into Michael.

"Hey," Michael blurted out. "What's going on? Magic, what are you doing on the bed?" Michael sat up, hitting his head against the headboard. Michael glared at me as I stood transfixed, staring at Magic's torso scrunched up against his legs. Magic looked perfectly comfortable and bedded in for the night.

Michael's response was quick. "This is not going to work for me. No ménage-a-trois. Get him off our bed."

"Magic, off," I commanded hopefully, pointing my finger to the floor. He cocked his head and stared at me.

"Why?"

"Magic. Off." I said louder. This time he sprung off the edge of the bed and sat on the floor by my feet.

"You don't have to yell."

"Sorry, hon," I said to my stressed-out husband. "Go back to sleep. I'll deal with him."

Michael slid down onto the mattress and rolled over on his side.

Magic lifted his head, looking like a coyote, and howled. *"Want to sleep in your bed."*

"Quiet." Michael pulled a pillow over his head.

Magic recoiled. My irritation was diffused by his sad eyes and disappearing ears that folded into the back of his head. "You have to be quiet or we're both going to be in trouble." I floated my hand over his silky ears. His outstretched paw gently swiped my knee. "Please be a good boy, for just a minute," I whispered, locking eyes with him. "Dad will be out cold in less than thirty seconds. Wait for it, wait for it. Just a few more seconds…okay." I breathed a sigh of relief hearing Michael's rhythmic snore from the far side of the bed.

"Now, Magic, lie down," I whispered, pointing to the nest of blankets. Magic grunted but begrudgingly obeyed. I hopped into bed and reached over to turn off the light. I barely had time to fluff a pillow before he leaped up and trampled me, plopping down in a heap at the base of the bed. I froze, praying Michael wouldn't wake up. Uncomfortably cramped with my knees in my stomach, I tried to stretch out, but Magic was firmly planted in a ball. The more I pushed, the more he resisted until I caught him squarely in the rump with my foot and booted him off the end of the bed.

Shimmying toward the center of the bed, I created a fortress for Michael's territory that Magic couldn't breach. Magic, unhappy that he had been relegated to the floor for the second time, hopped back on the bed and scooched in against my back. I was sandwiched in between Michael and Magic, feeling heavy breathing from both sides. Magic licked my exposed neck, but I lay motionless, ignoring his pleas for attention. Unable to solicit a reaction, he nestled his head into the base of my neck. Even though I felt his itchy fur and was desperate to scratch my exposed skin, I drifted off to sleep, relieved he had finally conked out.

From a dream of lying on warm sand on an uninhabited tranquil beach, I was awakened to a swishing sound inside my ear. Oh, the wonderful sound of waves crashing. The sound grew louder. I could feel something wet swirling along the side of my face. Swatting my hand in the direction of my head as if squashing a bug, I caught Magic's head instead, his tongue buried in my ear.

"What?" I shot up in bed, squinting in the dark.

"Ouch! Wake up. I think there's a dog catcher in the closet."

"Magic. Lie down and go to sleep. What has you so freaked out?"

"I'll watch closet, you sleep."

Slipping into a deep sleep, I dreamt I was running a marathon, feeling the pain of each heel strike. I could see the finish line and heard the dull roar of the crowd. The blinding sun prompted droplets of sweat to run down my forehead and into my eyes. Only a little further. A little further. Hey, what happened to my rhythmic breathing pattern? The sound pulsating in my ears was more like a panting dog than my own breathing. What?

In my sleepy state, I opened my eyes and felt Magic's hot breath torch me. There he was, leaning over me, drooling. When I attempted to sit up, I clocked him in the forehead.

"Ouch. Ahhhhh. Get off me." He bounded to the end of the bed; his ears hinged so far back they looked they might fall off.

"Watching the closet is scary."

"Now what? Do you have to go potty again?"

Michael shot up in bed. "No, I don't have to go potty."

"I don't mean you. I'm asking Magic."

"What's going on now?" Michael demanded.

"I gotta let Magic out——he needs to pee."

"Oh, for the love of God," Michael muttered, and sank back into the mattress. I feared that Michael, fed up with Magic's antics, would ask me to return him to the rescue organization.

Magic made a quick dash to the door. I stomped off to let him out, disappointed that my epic dream of winning my first marathon didn't contain one shred of reality. He returned from the yard within minutes and pranced through the door.

"Whew. Dog catcher in the closet makes me have to pee."

Climbing into bed and pulling the covers over my head, I thought for sure the sun would be coming up at any moment. Magic jumped on the bed and nestled in between us. I sighed, recalling that I was the one who made the decision to adopt him. There was no one else to blame for the disruption but me. The poor dog had been traumatized from being abandoned by his owners, housed at a shelter, transported to another kennel, treated for kennel cough, neutered, and, finally, adopted by our family. Why couldn't I be more empathetic and less consumed about my own selfish need for one night of sleep?

I reached out and pulled him close to my chest, hoping he had finally calmed down. I clung to Magic tightly, relishing our quiet moment. I felt like there was a therapeutic heating pad gently warming my joints.

Sometime after I dozed off, I must have pushed a different button on the Magic heating pad because I woke in a pool of sweat. It felt like a sauna. I tossed the sheets high into the air to try capturing a cool breeze and then inched toward the edge of the bed to escape the heating pad-turned-furnace, but it continued to follow me like a heat-seeking missile. Oh my gosh, Magic! I placed my hands on his side, leaned in and shoved as hard as I could to distance myself from the source of the heat. Magic didn't budge, but the force of the push sent me backwards, toppling to the floor. Staring up at the edge of the bed, I saw the whites of his eyes peering down at me.

"Why are you down there?" Magic jumped off the bed and raked his paw over the sheet I had wrapped around me like a mummy. *"You hide, I seek. Love that game."*

With my coping skills evaporating as quickly as the sweat dripping down my back, I stood up and flung the damp sheet onto the dresser, crawled back into bed, and stretched out face down, comatose.

I don't remember where Magic slept the remainder of the night, but by morning, he occupied eighty percent of the bed. That was the defining moment I knew that bunking in with Michael and me was not an option. He needed a bed of his own.

I chalked up the second night of interrupted sleep, bouts of bark-ing, whining to go the bathroom, and bed-hogging fiasco to be part of

Magic's transition into the household. In my state of denial, I was convinced his inability to sleep through the night was an isolated incident. That clouded thinking should have been my first clue that sleep deprivation had already begun to affect my brain.

MY NEW BEDROOM

I had thought the first 48 hours of trying to manage Magic were exhausting but keeping up with his level of activity reached a new pinnacle by day three. Any hope I had for being revitalized with a good night's sleep was fading. So, on the third evening, I took Michael's cue at nine o'clock to turn in early. I followed him to the bedroom, brushed my teeth, and took off my makeup. Magic paced around the bathroom, awaiting a chance to swipe the toothpaste tube for a few minty licks. But with no food prospects in sight, the bedroom had to suffice for a score of used dental floss and abandoned lip balm. He couldn't resist sashaying over to the nightstand to sample the heavenly smelling creams and lotions, with a variety of yummy flavors such as warm vanilla and gingerbread spice. I knew which ones were his favorites based on the number of tooth indentations in the bottles.

With those distractions aside, he moved on to his next favorite pastime——the no snoring challenge. The objective: keep Michael awake. No snoring meant no sleeping, and no sleeping meant there might be time for attention or, even better, more play time. He had an agenda, and by golly he intended to follow through with it.

Magic's orchestrated moves guaranteed he would gain Michael's attention every time he played the game. The fact that my husband had a propensity to nod off within thirty seconds of hitting the pillow meant Magic didn't have to wait long to start his plan. That was an important factor given Magic's non-existent attention span.

Our bed was at the precise height for Magic's snout to nestle comfortably on the edge of the mattress, providing the perfect vantage point to nudge Michael's exposed elbow. Magic turned his head sideways and used his snout as a forklift to dig under the available arm, hoisting it high into the air. With a quick flick of his head, Michael's arm thrashed into orbit before flopping down onto the mattress.

"You awake?"

When the snoring continued, Magic repeated the gesture a couple more times. When that didn't prompt a response, he started licking Michael's arm, triggering an allergic reaction. Within minutes, a sticky trail of red bumps appeared where his bubble-gum tongue had swept Michael's forearm in one long stroke, like a child savoring an ice cream cone on a blistering summer's day.

"Yuck. Not like chicken."

Michael, on the verge of snoring again, rolled over and dug his fingernails across his irritated skin. Magic saw the opening and leaned in with another short lick for good measure.

Michael peered over the edge of the mattress and dangled his inflamed arm in front of Magic's muzzle. "Look, Magic. I'm all itchy now. I'll pet you if you stop licking me."

"Now?"

Michael's hand glided over Magic's velvet head and flattened ears and paused under his chin for a scratch before starting to nod off.

"That's it, one scratch?"

"Magic, lie down," Michael mumbled.

Magic, firmly rooted by the side of the bed, had no intention of giving up so easily.

"Not tired." Magic's tail swished across the tile.

Michael started snoring again.

"Sneak attack time." Magic jumped onto the end of the bed, startling Michael awake again.

"Aaaaaa, Magic, go-to-your-bed."

"Don't have one." Magic's ears rolled back as he watched Michael turn over.

"Magic, leave Dad alone," I instructed him. "I'm going to read for a little while and then I'll take you out to pee and you'll get your treat."

"Treat? When? Now?"

Magic jumped onto the end of the bed, crouched down on his haunches, and creeped forward slowly on all fours, demonstrating his Navy Seal crawl. He dragged his belly along the blanket, head bobbing, as he moved into position to execute his plan.

"Ror-ror-ror."

Startled by his guttural growl, I lost control of the magazine I was trying to read. It flopped down onto the bed covers. Despite my valiant effort to regain possession of the tousled periodical, Magic swooped in like a trained operative, grabbing the corner of the magazine and digging his claws into the blanket with an impish look in his eyes. He had set himself up for a fight.

"What are you doing?" I grabbed a corner of the magazine, the two of us locked in a game of tug-of-war. With one last thrust of his head, he pulled the magazine free and my body hurled backwards into the pile of pillows. Magic darted off the bed and shook the remains of my food magazine, leaving crinkled, torn pages in a scattered trail.

"Treat now?"

Michael, hearing all the commotion, rolled over and said, "Let me guess. Magic's not tired and looking for attention."

"Oh honey, thanks for being understanding."

"The night is young."

At ten o'clock, I took the dogs out to the backyard for their requisite pee. They eagerly followed me out the door, found their favorite spot, did their business, and bolted into the kitchen for a night cap treat. I reached for the joint health supplement, carefully shielding the bottle from Magic. Maddie swallowed the tab in one gulp and retreated to her bed. I lured Magic into our bedroom and dangled the treat over the makeshift bed.

"That's the treat? Doesn't smell right."

"Magic, come. Magic, sit." He gingerly stepped onto the blankets and sat down. "Good boy," I said as he scarfed down the tab, practically taking my fingers off.

"You call that a treat? Needs chicken."

Without further fanfare, I quickly hopped into bed, turned out my bedside light, and whispered to Michael, already asleep, "Enjoy dreamland, honey." All was going better than expected. I sighed, feeling relieved everyone was tucked in for the night.

Just as I was entering my own dreamland, I heard slurping and lip-smacking sounds, like someone was eating an ice cream cone. The noise grated on my nerves. I instantly went from sleepy to irritated.

"Magic, stop licking." The annoying slopping sound increased in speed and intensity. I looked over the side of the bed, barely able to see his head bobbing, tongue striking the floor.

"Can't stop."

"You're killing me, you've got to stop." A spike of adrenaline tempted me to leap out of bed and leave the room.

Magic rolled over on his back, looking for attention. *"Bored. Not tired."*

"Quiet," I whispered. "You're going to wake up Dad." Magic jerked his paws in the air twice, swished his torso from side to side, and then rolled over to resume the licking position. Before his tongue made contact with the floor, I leaned over the edge of the bed and grabbed his muzzle.

"Why are you doing that?" I asked a little too loudly.

"What's the problem now?" Michael snapped, rolling over to turn on the light.

"He's compulsively licking the floor," I shot back. "He must be stressed out or something. All I know is that I'm stressed out, too. If I knew what his problem was, I could do something about it. Remember when we brought Charlie home from the hospital? If he cried at night, we'd jump up, change his diaper, feed and rock him, and then put him back in his crib. But sometimes, he still cried. He couldn't tell us if he had a tummy ache or wanted to be held because he couldn't talk."

"Well, start channeling your inner dog whisperer or we'll never sleep again." Michael rolled back over and turned off the light.

I pointed my finger in Magic's face. "Another fine mess you've gotten me into."

"Mess? Where?"

Three times Magic joined me on the bed, either pushing me in the stomach with his outstretched paws or pelting me with his restless legs. The licks on my elbows and the guttural growls that woke me up every hour triggered a meltdown at three o'clock in the morning. Why did I think his antics tonight would be any different than on the previous night? I decided to add delusional to my self-described personality disorders.

Cursing, I dragged my fatigued body out of bed and retreated to the guest bedroom with the puppy insomniac prancing after me. I shut the door behind us, but the spare bedroom wasn't soundproofed. I worried that his thunderous barks might awaken the dead as well as my already stressed-out husband who wasn't wearing ear plugs. I pulled down the shades and plopped into the twin bed, hoping Magic would find refuge on the plush carpeting instead of on my feet. Those hopes were dashed. Within a matter of minutes, he curled up at the end of the bed. Drifting in and out of consciousness, I periodically sat up, scanning the bed to make sure he had not escaped to wake up Michael. Was I deranged thinking he could turn the doorknob with his mouth, pry it open with his claws or crash the door down?

Several hours later I awoke to a high-pitched whine. Bleary eyed, I made out Magic standing at the door. His ears were pitched forward, and he cocked his head, listening intently to sounds coming from the other side.

"Mom? Mom?" Charlie called. "Are you going to make us breakfast? And what are you doing in the guest room? Where's Magic?"

"Too many questions for me right now. What time is it?"

"Six-thirty."

"Can you check to see if Dad is still here? I could really use his help right now."

Magic, hearing Charlie's voice, scraped his claws down the center of the door.

"Hey. Stop that. I'll let you out, just a minute," I said, giving the stink eye to Magic. "Charlie, did Dad leave for work?"

"Oh, sorry, Mom. Yeah, his car is gone."

"Darn it." I didn't see the balled-up blanket that had spewed onto the floor. When my foot caught in one of the folds, I crashed to the ground. "My ankle. Owwww! Stupid dog." Magic came over to assess the damage and licked my arm wildly.

Sorry. Have to pee. Now. Magic pasted his torso against the door.

I stood up and slowly limped over to him. "Move over, Magic," I said forcefully. I pushed him to the side and pried the door open. He slipped out, bolting down the hallway.

"I think Magic needs to go potty," Charlie yelled.

"What's your first clue?" I cried. "I need a little help here."

"Okay. Let's go, Magic." I heard the patio door slide open. "Go potty, Magic," Charlie instructed before slamming the door shut.

I shuffled into the kitchen, favoring my abused ankle. "Thanks, sweetie."

Charlie stared at me. "Mom, you look terrible! Your eyes are bloodshot and what's with the dark circles? You have two different pj's on and why are you limping?"

"I twisted my ankle getting out of bed. He has so much puppy energy he kept me up half the night. Honestly, he's a terror. Don't even ask."

Magic hovered outside the door barking loudly. *I peed, how about a treat?*

"Just look at him, panting like a maniac. Would you let him in? I don't think I can face him right now."

Charlie swung the door open and Magic bolted inside as Seth wandered into the kitchen and pulled out a chair at the table.

"Sorry, guys," I said. "I'm afraid breakfast is only toast and cereal.

I'm not up for cooking. Um... there might be some muffins in the freezer. I'll check."

The boys downed blueberry oatmeal muffins and bowls of peanut butter granola and swiftly loaded their dishes into the dishwasher to distance themselves from their grumpy mother. Ten minutes later, they flew out the door and hopped into their carpool, leaving me with a dog that was about to be responsible for my first nervous break-down. I felt light-headed and my stomach rumbled. The thought of anything but a cup of tea left me nauseous. I filled the kettle with water and pulled a soothing chamomile tea bag from a metal box.

"Treats. Starving!"

Maddie charged into the kitchen when she heard the rattle of the canister.

"I know you're both hungry." I limped into the garage and collected their bowls. Heading back inside, I knew trouble was brewing when I didn't see Magic waiting for me at the doorway. In a panic, I rushed into the kitchen, spilling some of the dog food on the floor. Still holding the remaining kibble, I got there just in time to see our counter surfer scarfing up a leftover blueberry muffin in one enormous bite, paper included. Sporting a blueberry stuck to his paw, he repeatedly licked it, trying to erase the incriminating evidence from the crime scene. Not one crumb graced the plate, which looked as clean as if it had just been plucked from the dishwasher. How he hadn't pulled the plate down with the muffin or left a shred of food visible to the naked eye was a mystery. Had I not caught him in the act, I would have assumed one of the boys had taken the leftover muffin for a mid-morning snack.

Magic hurried over to the trail of kibbles and sucked them off the floor like a powdered vacuum at a car wash. He leaped into the air several times in rapid succession, throwing in several twists and barks. When I placed the bowl on the floor, he inhaled the rest of his breakfast in record time, gasping for breath after each lightning-fast swallow. Watching Magic in feeding-frenzy mode, I decided it would never be in my best interest to take the bowl away while he was eating. The thought of hanging a sign by his feeding area that said,

"Danger: Keep Hands and Feet Away from Moving Mouth" seemed like a good idea.

I joined both dogs outside while they went to pee again and quietly rejoiced when they returned to the house without incident. Other than a sore ankle, dark eye circles, and a vanished blueberry muffin, my day was moving right along.

I looked at the clock. Seven-thirty. *What? Only seven-thirty?* Surely the clock was wrong. Why was time moving so slowly? Exhausted, I slumped onto the couch and shut my eyes in hopes of a power nap.

"Are you tired?" Magic whined as my head drooped. To prove his point, he placed a paw on my stomach. There would be no napping on his watch.

"Time to play."

"Okay, okay," I whispered.

Staring at the clock, watching the second hand tick by each numeral, I realized I was losing my sanity. The nighttime chaos would continue unless I figured out how to get Magic to sleep through the night. I needed a workable plan. But how could I possibly brainstorm when my thought processes seemed to be as airy as a cone of cotton candy? Drifting backwards into the pile of over-stuffed cushions, I vowed to clear out the fluff and come up with a solution. All I needed was a few minutes of shut-eye.

"Hey, no sleeping."

The boom of his bark jerked me back into reality. The dog was relentless.

When you are pushed to the maximum level of frustration, it's amazing how many ideas pop into your head. I leaped off the couch, grabbed a pen and paper, and jotted my new plan in bold letters.

MISSION: SLEEP THROUGH THE NIGHT

I spent the next two hours strategizing. The plan had two goals to achieve for our household to sleep at night. Goal one was to determine where Magic would sleep. Would that location be in the kitchen with Maddie, in the kids' room, or in our room? What a silly question, I mused. Of course, he'd be in our room. I turned my attention to the type of bed he might like. Orthopedic, a comfy couch, pillow, or cushion——there were several choices to consider. I didn't care about the shape, size, or material as long as the new purchase kept him on his bed instead of ours. I already had serious doubts whether that was remotely possible.

Goal number two was planning and implementing an exercise routine for every day of the week. I listed the various daily activities that could drain the tireless energy that turned him into a windup toy on steroids.

I noted all the items needed to execute the plan but stopped short, remembering I had to leave Magic unattended to shop for the bed. I couldn't call our neighbor, Cynthia, to dog-sit again unless I was prepared to be her personal chef for the next two months. What could I do? I didn't want to entertain the daunting calamities that could happen in my absence, but the idea of being held prisoner in my own house quickly reinvigorated me.

There was only one solution. I would puppy proof the house, like baby proofing, only more extreme. I'd strip the house of all physical risk factors and put Magic on lockdown. Who was the prisoner now?

With a plan of action in hand, I applied concealer to the dark circles dominating my face and dressed in a t-shirt and camo-printed shorts, fully prepared to do battle. I closed all the doors and cleared the kitchen counters of food, condiments, and vitamins. Family room antiques and throw pillows were moved to the hall closet along with my favorite Persian rug. Drawers slightly ajar that he could wedge open were closed, one by one. Items like the television remote and shoes were stored out of reach. I pulled the drapes off the floor and rested them inside the windowsills to make sure he didn't mistake them for a new place to pee. I couldn't leave anything to chance. The whole exercise seemed pointless until I caught Magic counter surfing in the kitchen.

"Bad dog, Magic," I yelled across the room.

He slinked off the counter. *"Peanut butter. Yum."*

I took Magic for a long walk to empty his bladder and burn off some excess energy. The thought of leaving him in the house without supervision was nerve-racking, but I had taken the necessary steps to secure everything. With a cheerful smile, I patted him on the head and walked to the garage.

My first stop was the pet store, where I picked up dog toys and a toothbrush. Looking at the selection of beds, none met my expectations, nor did I think they would meet Magic's. I needed to buy the ultimate dog bed that would make him want to sleep in his space, not mine. But where could I find an enormous, therapeutic, reasonably priced super-sonic dog bed? A warehouse shopping club, of course.

The extra-large dog beds looked like a stack of fluffy buttermilk pancakes. I yanked one from the top of the pile above me. Two pancakes separated from the pack and hit me on the head. I reached out, catching the edge of one and quickly tucked a portion of it under my body before tumbling to the floor. Sprawled out, I scanned the area to see if anyone had witnessed my mishap. To my chagrin, there was an older man with a beard and gold-rimmed glasses standing ten feet away. He hurried over to lend his assistance.

"Wow, those beds look really heavy. You took a hard fall. Are you okay?"

"Yes, I'm fine," I replied, as I scrambled to a sitting position in the middle of the bed, trying to minimize my embarrassment. "Just wanted to test the firmness, you know, to make sure it's comfortable," I said, rolling from side to side.

"Mmm. Gotcha. Is that for you or the dog?" he asked, chuckling.

"I may be figuring that out tonight."

I wrestled the bed into the shopping cart, checked out, dashed to the parking lot, and jammed it into the car. Filled with at least twenty pounds of stuffing, the bed occupied the entire trunk. The purchase of a bed fit for a prince had been successfully completed. I mentally checked off the first goal of Mission: Sleep Through the Night.

The first task had been relatively easy. The second one, devising a rigorous exercise schedule, seemed a little more daunting. How could I tap into the geothermic energy of a young, spirited lab? Driving home, I mapped out the day's activities, hoping Magic would be the only one completely worn out by the end of the day. Exhilarated at how my plan was progressing, I daydreamed about the blissful night of sleep awaiting me. I rolled down the window and shouted, "Let the games begin!"

As I pulled into the garage, I could hear Magic woofing at an ear-piercing level. Praying that I had been successful at puppy-proofing the house, I nervously opened the door leading to the foyer. He was in full bombardment mode as I entered, springing off his hind legs and snapping at the air like he was catching flies.

"Magic, sit. Magic, down. Were you a good boy?" I said multiple times walking into the family room, doing a loop through the great room, inspecting floors, and looking for signs of carnage. Everything was intact and there was no sign of pee to be found. "Magic, okay. Good boy!"

He danced across the foyer into the kitchen.

"Magic, I'm going to eat some lunch and then we'll spend the afternoon playing around in the pool. Sound good?"

"Lunch? Sounds great."

As I diced chicken breast, Magic crashed on top of my feet in hopes of catching any morsels falling off the cutting board. I gulped down a sandwich and guzzled a glass of herbal iced tea. When I stacked the plates in the dishwasher, Magic raced over to lick them clean.

"Yum. My favorite. Chicken."

While Magic was preoccupied with the pre-wash, I dashed into our bedroom closet and pulled out a swimsuit in preparation for the next activity. But as I was getting ready to put it on, Magic bounded into the closet, grabbed the suit, and dashed off.

"Fine," I murmured. Forget the suit, shorts will work. *Lauren, don't get sidetracked or upset. He's obviously in need of physical exercise. I have a plan to address that issue, so get moving.*

I walked out of the bedroom, picked up a pair of sunglasses, and headed toward the patio door. Magic and Maddie began a celebratory dance, jumping on each other, yapping, trying to muscle their way to be the first one out the door. A mass of paws, wet noses, and wagging tails circled around me. When I slid open the door, the dogs charged out onto the pool deck and sprinted toward the green plastic toy box. Magic arrived first and spun around in circles as though trying to catch his tail. As I reached into the toy box, Magic dove over me, whisking a frayed tennis ball into his mouth. Maddie ran beside him, hoping to dislodge the ball from Magic's clenched jaw.

He made laps around the pool, enjoying the chase. My plan was working better than I imagined. I figured fifteen laps equaled a quarter of a mile so after twenty passes I stopped counting. When Maddie gave up the chase, Magic trotted over and dropped the ball in front of me. Panting, with a muzzle frosted in slobber, he barked, flinging white foam onto my legs.

"Throw it, throw it, throw it."

"Magic, stop barking."

"Can't, too excited."

"Magic, sit."

Magic begrudgingly lowered his hind end to the ground. With his eyes fixated on the ball, only his lower abdomen moved, slightly bellowing in and out with his shallow breathing.

I hurled the gooey ball into the deep end to move the game forward. "Gross," I mumbled. Both dogs dashed to the side of the pool and sailed over the water, landing with such force that a large wave soaked me. In no time at all Magic retrieved the ball, hopped out of the pool, and spit the soggy mass at my feet. Maddie couldn't compete with Magic's retrieving skills, so she turned her attention to pulling Stealth, the floating chlorinator, around the shallow end.

Ninety-eight, ninety-nine, one hundred. One hundred retrievals from the pool in less than an hour. I thought my arm would fall off. Not bad for someone who was severely lacking in sleep and a dog who had learned to swim just days ago.

I yelled, "Game over," and stuffed the ball back into the toy bin. As I toweled the dogs' matted fur, I noticed Magic's belly had swelled to the size of a watermelon. Had he swallowed two gallons of pool water? I guess so. I left them both outside to bask in the sun, hoping their coats would dry so I wouldn't have to endure wet dog smell inside the house. The odor, a combination of stewed cabbage, a brewery, and cup of sour milk, was less than pleasing. Ten minutes later, Magic pawed at the glass door.

"Sorry, Magic," I said, rolling it open. "I know you don't like me closing the door, but it's over a hundred today. Not good for the air conditioning bill. Do you need to pee before you come in?"

"Yup. Drank too much pond water."

"Why don't you go and christen a few bushes?"

Magic sprinted to the closest shrubbery, lifted his leg, and soaked the lower branches.

"Okay, good job."

He dashed back into the house and sat by the pantry door. *"Time for a treat?"*

"So far today, you've been a very good boy." I reached into the pantry and pulled out chicken treats. "You're probably starving after all that swimming."

"Yes. Starving."

"Magic, sit. Good dog. Here you go." I tossed a couple into the air.

"Delicious. But only two?"

Resigned that he had maximized his treat quota, he horizontally stretched out on the tile, looking tuckered out.

While prepping dinner, I called his name to keep him from napping every time his eyelids closed. Fortunately, I didn't have to be on dog duty too long before I heard a car pull into the driveway. Magic sprang to his feet in super-alert mode to take down the possible invaders. My knight without shining armor, but with a huge set of chompers, manned his post to defend the fortress.

I stopped chopping chocolate and looked over at Michael as he walked into the foyer.

"Hi honey," I said, greeting him with a smile.

Before Michael could reply, Magic plunged forward, knocking an opened water bottle out of his hand. Water spewed across the floor. "Maaaggggiccc!" Michael yelled. Magic jumped several times before colliding with Michael's briefcase. When the case fell to the floor, folders, pens, and papers, scattered. Michael's foot caught an edge. He lost his balance and fell on his butt, crushing the water bottle. I ran into the foyer just in time to see the remaining liquid shoot out of the bottle like a firehose, drenching his trousers. He looked like he peed in his pants. I covered my mouth so Michael couldn't see my toothy grin.

Magic barked victoriously. He had disarmed the intruder. Over uproarious yips, Michael yelled, "Magic, off! Stop licking me. I'm going to get hives again. Lauren, help! Did Magic get any exercise today?"

"Of course, he did," I said, pulling on Magic's collar to save my husband from dog saliva. "I had him in the pool for over an hour. I've been exercising him all day. Well, it feels like all day. But listen, I've got great news. Our problem with puppy-induced sleepless nights is solved. This morning I came up with a new plan."

I paused. Looking at my husband lying on the floor, straddled by

Magic, and sporting a soaked crotch, I quickly determined that it was not the right time to talk about my ingenious idea.

Michael, disgusted at the chain of events, got up off the floor, collected his belongings and his dignity, and trudged into the bedroom. Magic trotted behind him, picking up a tennis shoe en route to the closet. Michael slipped on a pair of shorts and a t-shirt, grabbed a pair of socks and the lone sneaker, and returned to the kitchen. As Magic pranced by Michael, the shoe swung from side to side, pelting him in the legs and delivering alternating blows to his muzzle.

"Do you think he is trying to tell me something?" Michael asked. "Does this dog ever tire? What is he, bionic? We're too old to have a super-charged dog. Just watching him makes me exhausted. And the crazy stunts he pulls, oh, don't get me started."

Magic whisked away one of Michael's socks before performing an airborne three sixty, landing on all fours.

"Magic, come," Michael said.

Magic sauntered over and slowly looked at Michael. He paused for a few seconds before depositing the sock at Michael's feet.

"Good dog." Michael looked over at me. "That was amazing. How did that happen? He listened to a command. Maybe he's trying to butter me up because he wants something. Like a scratch under the neck, or a walk."

Did you say walk? Let's go! Magic eased forward on his front legs.

"Magic, down," Michael said confidently. "Hmmm…maybe I should try a new activity, like a bike ride."

"Oh, great idea! I bet Magic would love that," I gushed. "We need to find ways to wear him out, drain him of all of his energy. That's part of the new strategy I came up with this morning, Mission: Sleep Through the Night."

Michael made a face.

"One of the goals is to make sure he is physically exhausted by the end of the day."

"Okay, you convinced me. It's my turn. I'll take him out for a spin. Do you think he'll be alright in this heat? Maybe I'll circle the neighborhood a few times. That way, if he gets too hot, the house won't be far away."

"He'll be fine, it's not as hot as it was earlier this afternoon. He obviously needs to run and burn off more energy." I looked at my watch. "The boys won't be home until after soccer practice. You'll have plenty of time to ride and shower. I'll shoot for dinner at seven-thirty. And I'm making your favorite, Thai salmon stir-fry in orange sauce with pasta, asparagus, bell peppers, and carrots——and for dessert, a chocolate peanut butter pie. That should make everyone happy."

"Mmm. Good thing I'm going to burn off a few calories." Michael walked toward the garage with Magic at his heels. He started to turn the doorknob, but Magic's paws slammed into his back. "Magic, off. You're so excited I can hear your teeth chattering. Calm down. Magic, sit, Magic, stay. You need to wait."

"Can't wait." Magic whined until Michael returned from the garage wearing a securely fastened bike helmet. Magic smacked his front paws into Michael's chest as he came in. *"I'm ready. Hurry."*

MISSION: MALFUNCTION

"Whoa! Magic, off," Michael boomed, trying to dodge the energetic lab's repeated leap into his side.

"Lauren," Michael pleaded. "Would you put Magic's harness on and bring him outside? I need a few minutes to prepare mentally and physically for this activity. Maybe I should put on knee and elbow pads? Maybe follow me in the car in case we crash?"

"Michael, why are you so nervous? You're taking our dog for a bike ride, not riding him. Stop acting like you're a jockey in the Kentucky Derby."

"You don't get it. He's on a leash, which means we're physically connected. What happens if he starts to pull me? I'm the one holding the reins. Look at him, snorting and bouncing around the kitchen. Don't you think he looks like a horse getting ready to be led into a starting gate? Forget a leisurely lap around the hood. Please say a prayer for me," Michael begged. "Good luck getting on his harness. I'll meet you outside."

Wrestling Magic to the ground to put on his harness on brought back the chaotic memories of our first meeting at the kennel. Maybe it was asking too much of Michael to take him on a bike ride. No. I had exercised Magic in the pool and tired him out. Michael would be fine. I cinched up the sides of his harness as if tightening the girth of a saddle.

Magic spied the leash in my hand and exploded like a rocket being launched into the next galaxy. *"Where we going?"*

"Sit, Magic," I shouted over the booms of barking as he did donuts around the kitchen table. I reached out to grab him but missed, swiping the air. "Magic, come."

Slowing down to a jog, he ambled over to me with ears raised high on his head. I leaned in and snapped on the leash, and within a split second he sprinted for the front door, dragging me behind him.

"Sit, Magic. I'm not opening the door until you sit." Magic's eyes shifted from the door handle to me. "Magic, sit," I said a little louder.

"Too excited." Magic's eyes again bounced from the door handle to me. He cocked his ears and half-heartedly skimmed his backside along the floor. I opened the front door and gave him the okay command. He bolted onto the sidewalk, looking for Michael. Hanging on to the leash with every ounce of strength I could muster, I dug my heels into the pavers to gain traction, barely able to keep upright as he charged forward.

Magic's jaw quivered with excitement at the sight of Michael's bike. A stream of high-pitched barks erupted. *"Let's gooooo."*

I passed off the leash to Michael and watched as the two barreled down the driveway. "Be careful!" I yelled. I wondered if Michael heard anything but the pounding of his heart and Magic's incessant barking. Was it too soon to call an ambulance?

Twenty minutes later, Michael stumbled through the front door with sweat dripping off his chin. Magic walked slowly behind, his long tongue jetting in and out in cadence with his panting.

"That dog is a lunatic," Michael exclaimed. "I'm lucky I survived. Hanging onto the leash and the handlebar at the same time is tough, but at lightning speed? It's death-defying. He was out in front sprinting the whole time. If he'd stepped in front of the tire I would've been flung over the handlebars and Magic would've been flattened by the bike. I hate to think of what would've happened if I wiped out. Broken bones, road rash. Ugh." He paused, out of breath. "We were tearing around corners. Good thing there weren't any cars. For the first five minutes I couldn't pedal fast enough to keep up with his pace. I never thought he could run like that. He really was like a race-horse coming out of the gate." Michael sighed and peered over at Magic. "Well, at least he looks tired. You know what we say. A tired lab is a good lab. But I have to believe there's a safer way to exercise him."

"Bike ride, fun." Magic crashed on his side, stretched out his legs like wooden pegs, and sunk his hot fur against the cool tile. His tongue spilled onto the floor as his chest heaved up and down.

"Oh my gosh, Michael, I'm glad you're okay. You really took one for the team. Thanks for your help. I've barely had enough energy to keep up with him. If I don't get some sleep tonight, I'm going to be a basket case. I think there needs to be one more activity before bedtime to make sure he's dog-tired."

Michael raised his eyebrows.

"Seriously, maybe we can toss the Frisbee a few times after dinner."

"Lauren, can I take a shower first?"

"Sorry. Of course."

I went on autopilot making dinner that evening, abandoning my plan to make Michael's favorite dish. I threw together whatever left-overs I had in the refrigerator. Charlie and Seth, starving after playing soccer for two hours, didn't complain when I served cold grilled tri-tip, reheated mashed potatoes, and microwaved snow peas. Fortu-nately, there were raspberry truffle brownies in the freezer that satis-fied everyone's sweet tooth, even if they were hard as a rock when I served them. Magic continued to snooze on the family room tile, allowing me to give my full attention to the family.

After plates were cleared and stacked in the dishwasher, Charlie and Seth took the dogs to the backyard for a quick game of keep away. Everyone returned hot and thirsty.

"I still can't believe how lightning-fast Magic is when he wants a toy. He practically bowled me over before I had a chance to catch the ball," Seth said.

"Yeah, poor Maddie just stood in the middle hoping Magic would drop it," Charlie added. "He's quite the athlete."

"Yes, I've noticed that, too," I said winking. "Enough playing around guys, time for homework."

"Okay," they said and headed for their rooms.

Michael put down the newspaper. Magic, standing by his bowl, licked his lips to stop the trickle of water spilling onto the floor. "Lauren, I think Magic's ready for another round of activity."

"You're kidding, right? He just finished playing a game with the boys. Don't you think he needs some recovery time?"

"Does he look like he needs recovery time? He polished off a quart of water and looks good to go. Is there anything about his body language that says he's not interested in playing anymore? No worries, I've got this. Why don't you put your feet up and read while I take our windup toy out for one last game of Frisbee?"

"Okay, thanks," I replied. "Remember to take a towel to clean off the slobber. It's really hard to throw that thing when it's slimy."

Michael retrieved the Frisbee from the closet and placed it on the edge of the table. Magic snapped into play mode as if the first game of the day was ready to unfold. He made a beeline for the red disk, swooping in to pick it off the table. Michael, seeing two wild eyes and a hurtling mass of dog, whisked the saucer into his hand and walked toward the patio.

"Game on," he taunted.

Magic waged a doggie temper tantrum. *"Want it. Now."*

Michael gripped the Frisbee in one hand, holding it high in the air while trying to open the door with the other hand. While Magic jumped into the air, Michael clenched the disc and grabbed the door handle with both hands, prying the door open. Magic saw his chance. He dove forward, swiped the Frisbee out of Michael's grasp, and charged through the doorway, disappearing into the backyard.

"Told you I wanted it."

"Magiiiiic!" Michael bellowed, running after him.

The door banged shut. Alone at last, I picked up a magazine from the coffee table, collapsed onto the leather couch, and thumbed through the pages. I questioned my judgment. *Did I make the right decision adopting Magic or was bringing him home a huge mistake?* I bit my fingernails as my thoughts whirled. *Would Mission: Sleep Through the Night work?* I felt pressured to find a solution for his disruptive behavior. I had found the perfect dog bed and exercised our energetic lab, but what if that didn't work? I would be a zombie from lack of sleep and my family would be angry that I brought home a dog that was undermining all semblance of order in the household. Not a pretty combination with no immediate fix. I looked out on the patio and saw Michael hosing off the goopy slobber Magic had flicked onto his upper body. A new question loomed as I opened the door. *Who was this dog?* Three days into the adoption, I had no idea.

Magic bounded in, panting, still wet in the places Michael missed with the towel. "Eww, Magic, your muzzle is sticky." I backed up, trying to dodge his attempt to scent me with his muzzle.

"You smell delicious. Like chicken."

Michael walked into the house and closed the door behind him.

"Thanks, honey," I said. "This is the second time tonight you helped me out. I know he's a challenge——I'm doing everything I can to get him to settle in but..."

"I know you're working with him. He's obviously got a lot of energy to burn."

"Yeah, he wore me out. I can barely keep my eyes open. I'm so delirious I almost forgot to debut Magic's new bed. Remember we talked about him not having his own bed? I'm sure that's the reason he bunked in with us. Anyway, the warehouse club had an awesome one. He's going to love it."

I turned to Magic, who was still panting heavily. "Oooh, Magic," I said with as much enthusiasm as I could muster. "I bought something very special for you, but you have to stay here until I return from the garage."

Beaming, I dragged the monster-sized bed behind me into the family room. Magic trotted over and stretched out his neck to sniff the cargo. Before he had a chance to reject the purchase, I carried it into our bedroom and dropped it by my bedside, thinking he might feel more secure if he slept near me. He followed closely to get a better view of his new bunk. The stuffing looked so inviting that I leaned over and purposely fell into the center of the cushion. Curling into the fetal position, I monopolized every inch of the surface.

"Oh, Magic, this is soooo comfy," I crooned. "You're going to like this. Can I sleep here tonight?"

"Don't like it." With one quick hop, Magic jumped up on the edge of the bed.

"Really, Magic? This is how it's going to be?" He peered down at me. "You're impossible!" I rocked back and forth a couple of times to gain enough momentum to stand. I brushed dog hair off my shorts and swiftly exited the bedroom. "I'm so frustrated!" I blurted out, stomping into the family room where Michael was sitting.

Magic sprang off the bed and followed me, howling loudly. *"Sorry, don't sleep on dog beds."*

The first goal of Mission: Sleep Through the Night had failed. Now, my efforts to find a suitable dog bed had been thwarted. I was exhausted after participating in the circus Magic had made of our household.

Charlie and Seth heard the commotion and busted out of their rooms, tracking me down in the family room.

"Why are you yelling? And why's he barking again?" Charlie asked.

"I know why," Seth chimed in. "Because Magic's crazy." Seth looked over at me. "He's causing all kinds of problems — you're sort of losing it, Mom. Even though you said you'd make breakfast this morning, I was glad you didn't because you might've started a fire."

I sighed. "Sorry, guys. I need to be more patient with Magic, but life seems a lot more complicated with him around. I have to remember he's not only a rescue but he's an eleven-month-old lab with puppy-mania. That's a double whammy." I sighed again. "Your dad and I are trying to get him settled, but that isn't going to happen overnight. I'm as frustrated with the situation as you are."

"Mom, why do you want to keep him?" Charlie asked. "He pulls your arm out the socket when you take him for a walk and keeps you up all night. Who knows if he's even a lab? Well, okay, he does look like one, but we don't know where he came from and he didn't end up in a shelter because he was a good dog, right?" Charlie folded his arms across his chest, turned, and looked toward his room.

"Wait. Listen, guys. I'm sorry Magic has been such a problem. He's obviously having a hard time adjusting to his new life. Can you be a little more understanding for the next few days? I'll try to be present, but I haven't had much sleep over the last few days and, based on his behavior, I don't know when I will."

"Fine," they both said, rolling their eyes.

"Thanks." I hugged the boys good-night and suggested they take up my offer of a pair of ear plugs. They grimaced and headed to their rooms, ignoring my recommendation.

I turned to look at Magic lying on the floor, compulsively licking the tile. "Magic, go to your bed. I need a break from you." I watched him wander into our bedroom.

I picked out a comfy area of the couch, closed my eyes, and sank backwards into the plush pillows. The word 'foolish' slipped out of my mouth. *Lauren, don't act so surprised. Like I didn't see this coming? I barely survived the daytime battle of wills between Magic and me. Why did I think our nighttime clashes would be any different?* The idea of Magic's sleeping behavior being altered by conforming to my demands was a fantasy. I shook my head, trying to clear the cobwebs. The last time I recalled having brain fog this badly was when our fussy newborns required endless hours of walking from one end of the house to the other all night long. Maybe the kids were right, and I was losing my mind. Comparing a newborn baby to Magic could only be attributed to one thing: sleep deprivation. Things were worse than I thought. *Focus. Focus, Lauren.*

Mission: Sleep Through the Night wasn't a total loss, yet. Even though the dog bed hadn't been well received at the first introduction, there had to be a way to convince him to sleep on it. On the bright side, the pool games, bike ride, and Frisbee session had been successful in depleting, if only temporarily, his puppy-like exuberance.

With a renewed spirit, I pushed myself off the couch and marched into the bedroom. Magic, curled up on our bed, looked extremely comfortable. I started to think his new bed was going to be a sleeping option for me.

"Magic, I told you to go to *your* bed."

"This is my bed."

I took a big breath. *Don't lose your cool, Lauren. Try reverse psychology.* "Magic, is it okay if I crash on your bed tonight?" I slowly lowered my butt onto the foam mattress, wiggled back and forth and curled up into a ball. "Oh, Magic, this bed is soooo nice. Are you sure you don't want to sleep here?" I asked enticingly.

Perched on the bed with paws hanging over the edge, he yowled. I thought, *Yeah, progress.* At least he wasn't barking. But his attention to my wooing was short-lived. Magic was perfectly content to maintain the position he had assumed.

"Like your bed."

"What? After all my painstaking efforts to find you the perfect bed. What is wrong with you?" I said, fuming as I stood and walked into the bathroom to get ready for bed.

His ear-less face appeared at the bathroom doorway where he sat and watched with droopy eyes while I washed my face. *"Sorry."*

Lathered up in soap, I couldn't look at him, nor did I want to.

"Magic, Maddie, let's go out to pee," Michael called from the family room.

Magic's ears popped up. He turned his head toward the bedroom then back to me shifting his weight from one paw to another, as if he was deciding whether to run outside to pee or stay with me in the bathroom. Nature won out. He zoomed out of the bathroom.

I dried my face and walked into the adjoining closet to put on my nightshirt.

Magic peed in a flash and returned to the house. *"Here I come."*

In less than a minute, I could hear Magic running at breakneck speed. His toenails skimmed the floor trying to gain traction around the bed. I guessed he was in hot pursuit of something. Whatever it was, I knew it couldn't be good, so I dove for my nightshirt, pulled it over my head, and rifled my arms through the sleeves. As I turned around, I caught a glimpse of him bursting into the bathroom.

"Not here? She must be where that big water bowl is." He checked out the toilet area. *"Not here either? Gotta find her."*

I watched his tail snare the end of the toilet paper roll, flinging it into the toilet bowl. That's when he saw me. *"Whoops."*

There was a blur of fur and wide-open eyes running toward me at a feverish pace. I prepared for the impact of a car crash. He pushed off his back legs and leaped forward, hurling his brawny body in my direction. Dirty feet stamped my chest, leaving paw prints on my nightshirt. Magic slipped to the ground, regained his balance, and charged forward with outstretched feet straight into my stomach. He finished by dragging his paint brush paws in two parallel rows down the front of my nightgown. Magic's feet hit the ground. He stumbled but sprang into action, rocking back on his hind legs like a wild-eyed stallion. As he fell forward, I leaned back, trying to dodge the attack, but the weight of his body caught me in the stomach, pressing me against the wall-mounted shoe rack. I reached back but my flailing hands wiped out an entire row of shoes. I screamed as a cascade of handbags flew off the shelves and plummeted to the floor. Stilettos, strappy sandals, and pumps rained down on my head and pelted Magic. Designer bags and straw summer purses scattered.

Standing in the middle of the wreckage, Magic stared into my eyes. *"Found you."* He extended his neck, preparing to lick my arm, but stopped short and waved his nose high into the air. *"New shoes. Smells delicious. Not like chicken."*

"Magic!" I yelled. "Are you crazy? Did you think we were playing hide and seek?"

"You hide, I seek."

"We were not playing a game. What's your problem?"

"Wanted to find you."

"Enough already." I put my hands on my hips. "Magic, down. Magic, stay. I'm not happy with you right now." Magic's paws bumped into a leather purse as he slowly sank to the floor. Surveying the disheveled closet, I shook my head.

Michael ran into the closet. "What just happened? I took the dogs out to pee and all hell broke loose."

"Yeah, not exactly how I saw the evening coming to a close either," I said, rolling my eyes. "This dog is going to be the death of me. How are we going to get him on any kind of schedule if we can't get him to settle down at night, or for that matter, anytime during the day? I'm trying hard not to lose it, but I'm running out of patience."

Magic caught my gaze and raised one eyebrow as his tail started to thump against the shoe boxes.

I looked over at Michael. "I don't know what to do," I whispered. "I'm sorry. I have really made a mess of things. He's disrupted the boy's studying with his fretful barking and made me a candidate for the funny farm. He's disturbing everyone's sleep." My eyes shifted over to Magic. "Don't give me that impish grin, Mr. Troublemaker. You made a mess of things tonight."

Magic's tail wagged faster. *"Didn't mean to."*

"See, this is what always happens. I want to stay mad at him but he's so darn cute. Just look at those sad eyes and droopy ears."

"Stay here, honey. I'll get the rug cleaner and some rags. Please don't worry about this. Everything's going to be okay. Nobody sees our closet anyway."

Michael cleaned up the mud-stained carpet and then climbed into bed. As I re-arranged the closet, I started thinking. *Face the facts, Lauren. I'm going to have to take off more than a week of work to get Magic settled into the household. Who am I kidding? Based on everything that's happening, I may need six months of leave. Six months? I may have to stay home permanently to keep Magic out of trouble. Ohhh, why did I adopt this dog? Because I wanted a playmate for Maddie. Don't get all wigged out. Why not stay home with him? That would solve the problem. Maybe, but if I stop cooking professionally, how will I be able to fill my foodie passion? Well, it's not that I wouldn't be cooking anymore. I have family and friends I can feed. Think Lauren, think. What if I hosted cooking classes at my house, or in a client's kitchen? That would be different and fun. Actually, that could be the perfect part-time job. If I hold class during the evening or weekend, Michael and the kids could supervise Magic. I know I'll miss cooking for clients in the appliance showroom but, teaching people how to cook could be just as rewarding. There's a lot to think about. I've also got to factor in what might happen if I leave Magic alone every day while at work. Will I be stressed out worrying about what he got into or peed on? Of course I will.*

My plan to find a playmate for Maddie was not turning out like I had hoped. Magic watched intently until the last shoe and purse was placed on the shelf. I looked over at him, gave him the stink eye and said, "Thanks to you, this messed up nightshirt has to go into the laundry. And guess what, I don't know if it's going to come out in the wash."

"That's a problem?"

"Magic, come," I said sternly. He slowly stood up, dropped his head and followed me out of the closet and into the bedroom. Remorseful, his ears were pasted so far back I could barely see them. I pointed my finger at him.

"Magic, bed," I whispered.

"Okay."

I watched as he gingerly stepped onto his bed, circled, and plopped down, forcing out a grunt. He looked defeated. I bent down and scooped his silky head into my hands. Looking deep into his eyes, I pleaded, "Magic, you have to stop being such an instigator. You're making the whole family angry. I want to make this work, but I need some help. I'm thinking of turning in my resignation so you won't be left alone. Maybe I'll just re-invent my cooking career. If I do that, will you promise me you'll be on better behavior?"

Was I really trying to reason with a dog? Did I actually say out loud that I needed his help? Maybe I was the one who needed help.

Magic's eyes glassed over. *"Need you."*

15

MISSION: DENIED

The question of why Magic became frenzied when he couldn't find me in the bathroom was seriously concerning. I feared his behavioral issues were going to be more than I could manage. Were his reactions a result of being displaced as a puppy, a reflection of his difficulties adjusting to his new life with us, or something more serious? Even though Patti, our intake coordinator, had talked about separation anxiety, I wanted to dismiss the idea that Magic could have that condition. Magic sat on his bed facing me, flicking his ears back and forth. I lifted the top sheet, slipped onto the comfort of the cool mattress, and clicked off the light. Sinking my head into the pillow felt heavenly. On the verge of dreamland, I heard Magic's collar rattle. Opening my eyes slowly brought the room into focus. Magic's feet shuffled in my direction, followed by the sound of his tail hitting the mattress. *"You asleep?"*

"Shhhhh." I rolled over onto my side, reaching to turn on the light. "Don't wake up Dad. Now what?"

The facial frown I hoped would send him back to bed had no effect. Dropping his ears, he licked his lips and slinked closer, inches from my face. His eyes caught the light. There I was, face to face with a dog in relentless pursuit of my attention. Hadn't I been patient and attentive to his needs for what seemed to be weeks? I just wanted some sleep.

Magic continued his stare. *"Pet me."*

I wanted to scream but his meek expression deflated my anger. How could I be so insensitive to a dog showing signs of distress? More than anything, I wanted to help Magic but had no idea what to do. I felt alone in my struggle. I rolled over on my back and stared at the ceiling, searching for answers. I could feel the mattress dip where he gently rested his muzzle. Warm air from his nose tickled my elbow. I eased my hand over the silky fur of his ears, and then down his neck, kneading the velvety soft scruff with my fingers. His eyes grew heavy as he sank to the floor. I hoped that maintaining one hand on Magic's flank would help him feel secure enough to drift into sleep. "Good job," I whispered.

Minutes later, my hand shot into the air when he popped up into a sitting position. I ignored him, moving my arm onto the edge of the mattress. I felt the pad of his paw brush across my arm until sweetly resting in the crook of my elbow. Determined to get my attention, he tickled my skin with lingering tongue sweeps that activated goose bumps up and down my forearm. I thought surely he would tire of licking my gingerbread scented body lotion. Wrong. The tingle from the ginger must have been an added bonus. When I started counting the number of licks instead of sheep, I knew a new game plan was needed. With one giant thrust I pushed back the covers, rolled off the edge of the mattress, and dropped to the floor, landing next to him.

Magic fluttered his ears and wagged his tail. *"On the floor with me? Great. Want to pet me?"*

"Magic," I said, whispering, "you're so frustrating. I don't want to give up on you, but I'm at a loss for what to do next."

How could I help him manage his anxiousness when I couldn't even control my own anxiety when I participated in *Iron Chef* competitions? I should have known his disposition wouldn't be any different than what I had witnessed at the kennel. I was annoyed at his behavior, but who was to blame? Me. I'm the one who brought him home. It's not that I didn't think there would be challenges adopting Magic, but they had become trials of epic proportions. My determination to make the adoption work was starting to ebb. Magic was testing my insecurities. I was wading deep into the unknown territory of an emotionally scarred rescue dog. *Lauren, hang on to your convictions. Follow through on this adoption. Stay committed.* But how can I make it right for him when I can't make it right for myself?

"Alright, Magic," I said, reaching out to stroke his ears, "I may have gotten myself into this mess, but you have to help me get out of it. The first way you are going to help me is to let me sleep."

"Okay. But I sleep with you." He tenderly placed his paw over my arm. I petted him with slow strokes, starting at the side of his neck where the fur fluffed out of his collar.

I tried to understand Magic's behavior from his perspective. How could I blame him for his inability to adjust to his new life when he was still coping with the stress of being adopted?

His body relaxed as I let my fingers rest on his chest. After ten minutes of sitting with him on the hard tile, I thought Magic's sleepy eyes might be a signal he was ready for bed. I looked at the clock. One in the morning? No, couldn't be. I stood and pointed in the direction of his bed. Begrudgingly, he stepped on it, circled four times to find the right spot, and plopped down. He looked as dejected as if I had marooned him on a castaway island.

With Magic in his bed at last, I climbed onto the mattress and drifted off to sleep. I was so spent that, short of an earthquake, I wasn't going to wake up. Sometime during the night, our needy canine jumped onto our bed and nestled in between us. Either passed out or unwilling to resume battle, I didn't force him off. Mission: Sleep Through the Night was never talked about again. He had won the battle of wills and with his victory he claimed our bed as his. So much for negotiating with a dog.

16

NAVY SEAL STRIKES AGAIN

The first two weeks Magic lived with us was like having a tornado incessantly touching down inside the house. Although the windows didn't shatter and the roof didn't blow off, the unpredictable winds and the speed at which our twister accelerated threw our household into turmoil. Thankfully, by the third week, the gale had died down, giving the family a chance to settle back into everyday life.

I made a family favorite dinner of baked ziti with pesto, Parmesan and ricotta; Caprise salad with yellow and red heirloom tomatoes, fresh mozzarella, chopped garlic, basil dressing, and fig balsamic; a crunchy loaf of freshly baked sourdough bread; and a flourless chocolate cake with mascarpone topping. As Charlie and Seth finished dessert, I started the conversation I had been avoiding for days.

"Hey everyone, we need to talk about Magic. Shouldn't take long, but it's important. I don't know if you remember, but the rescue gave me a twenty-one-day trial period to see whether Magic would be a fit for our family."

"I thought you already filled out adoption papers and paid the fee," Michael said.

"I did, but because he never went into foster care, the organization told me they would take him back after three weeks if we couldn't make it work." I looked around, trying to read facial expressions. "We've had Magic for the allotted trial period. I know, hard to believe, right?" I smirked. "Anyway, we need to make a group decision about whether to finalize his adoption." My voice cracked; I cleared my tightened throat. "But before everyone weighs in, I want to make a few comments." I sat back in my chair, not wanting to appear traumatized by the conversation. "I know better than anyone else sitting here at this table about the challenges this dog has rained on our family. I never thought I'd have to take extended time off of work just so I could supervise a dog. Who knows when I'll get back to my job?" I looked at the boys and took a big breath. "Do you remember our conversation about adopting a rescue? It couldn't have been more than a month ago, right?"

"I do," Charlie said.

"You guys said how much you wanted another dog." I raised my eyebrows. "You agreed to help take care of it. Well, the "it" happens to be Magic."

"Yeah, Mom, we did, but who knew our "it" would be so crazy? I mean, you've had to take off work."

"So, what are you saying? You want me to send him back? Does that mean you're reneging on your commitment?"

"Geez, Mom," Seth said. "Don't get all freaked out on us. I don't want to get rid of him——and yeah, I'll help out, but you have to admit, the last three weeks haven't been normal with Magic around."

I turned my attention to Michael. "I'm almost afraid to ask you what you're thinking."

"He's a handful. Can't deny that. Are you sure you want to do this? I'm not convinced anymore that Maddie needs a playmate."

I argued back, "I don't know, it seems as though Maddie's temperament has improved a lot since Magic's arrival. They're best buds. You want to break that up?"

"Yeah," Charlie said, "it's great to see Maddie back to her old self." He thought for a moment. "I think Dad's right that Magic is a nut case, but I'm kinda thinking he's our nut case. I really do want to keep him. He's part of the family now."

"Are you all sure about this?"

Seth broke the uncomfortable silence. "He does make more work for you because of all the stuff he gets into, and his barking is the worst, but he's a really fun dog. Remember last week when Dad had gone to bed and I stayed up throwing a ball around the family room for Magic?"

"I don't think this is the right time to bring that up," I pleaded.

Ignoring me, Seth continued. "And then I grabbed the ball, opened the door to your bedroom and threw it on the bed?" Seth and Charlie roared with laughter. "Dad had no idea what was happening. Magic pounced on the bed and raked his paws over Dad looking for the ball until he found it. Scared him half to death!"

The belly laughs from Seth reminded me of when he was a toddler. I tried to keep from laughing, letting out a snort instead.

"Hey, you two, this is supposed to be a convincing argument for keeping Magic," Michael said sarcastically.

"Sorry," Seth said. "But it was funny."

"Okay, back to our discussion. You guys already know how I feel. I want to keep him. He knows commands, I mean, at least he comes when you call him. You have to admit he listens better than Maddie."

"I don't know," Charlie said. "He may know his commands, but why does he bark his fool head off before listening?"

"I know he has issues but look at all the other wonderful qualities he has. Besides, I think the worst is behind us. Sending Magic back to the rescue would be tough on him, you know, with his behavioral quirks."

"Who else would put up with that?" Seth said.

I shook my head. "We're getting off track again."

"Dad, do you want to keep Magic?" Seth asked.

"I'm not sure my vote counts. I don't think there ever was a question of whether we would keep him because your mother made up her mind he was part of the family the day she met him at the kennel."

"Oh, Michael," I blurted out. "I told you after the first week I had doubts whether we should keep him."

"I think you said that because you were exhausted at the beginning. You never meant that."

"Yeah, you're probably right," I said quietly. "I know it's been hard on everyone, but please, let's not give up on him. I can't bear the thought of returning him to the rescue. Everyone okay with that?"

Everyone nodded.

Later that night, climbing into bed, Michael said, "I'm surprised you brought up whether we should keep him or not. I thought you had already made up your mind."

"I did."

"Then why did you ask how we felt?"

"Because I can't manage this dog alone."

Michael furrowed his brow. "Oh, and you think because we outnumber him, we'll have a better chance of survival?"

"Something like that."

I called Patti the next day to make it official.

Over the next week everything seemed to fall into place. The whole family participated in the daily exercise plan for Magic, leaving me some time to tackle household projects like gardening.

I loved flowers for their beauty and fragrance but wasn't enamored with having to change them out in the summer and fall because of the intense summer heat and cold winter nights. Nonetheless, the job of painstakingly re-planting twice a year was well worth the effort, even if the task did require transporting twenty-pound bags of potting soil from the car to the backyard. I put on my gardening gloves, unloaded the bags into the wheelbarrow, and got to work.

After the last flat of flowers was planted, I surveyed the finished project and smiled. Multi-colored petunias, orange African daisies, and yellow lantana dotted the pool, clustered in large pots. The colorful blooms and green foliage enhanced the pebble tec pool finish for a beautiful fall effect. Fall? Who was I kidding? The temperature was still hitting ninety degrees in the Phoenix afternoon sun.

Covered in potting soil and fertilizer, I headed to the house for a cool shower and glass of iced tea. I brushed off the excess dirt and started opening the patio door when I spied Magic peering around the side of the toy box.

"Hey, Magic boy," I said sweetly. "Whatcha doing?" He didn't make eye contact. "Are you hiding from me?"

"Shhhhh...duty calls."

"What's up?"

"It's a secret."

Magic licked his lips. His tail, close to the ground, wagged fast.

"I'm going to take a shower, but I'll leave the door open a little in case you want to come in."

After taking a long shower, I threw on a cotton dress, stepped into a pair of sandals, and combed my fingers through my wet hair. Entering the kitchen, I glanced around the room, expecting to see Magic searching for tidbits of food on the counter. No Magic. I looked out the patio door and froze, unable to process the scene in front of me. There was Navy Seal barking at one of the planted flowerpots. He grabbed the rim of a pot with his teeth, pushed it over and rolled the container along the deck, leaving a winding stream of black soil and a mass of trampled flowers.

"Noooo!" I yelled, ripping the door open and racing outside. Magic stopped in his tracks, like a cornered thief with no place to run. His paws and ears were matted with mud. His muzzle was dotted with white foam, making him look like he had gone face down in a bowl of popcorn.

"Maaagic!" What are you doing? Bad dog. Noooo… all that work, my flowers." I felt like a stick of dynamite ready to explode.

"Look, the area's safe now."

The thought of the cleanup, the hours of wasted energy, and the ruined flowers sparked every nerve in my body. This dog was infuriating. No, he was beyond infuriating. Why did he do the things he did? Pots lay strewn along the deck, cracked and broken. Seething, I walked over to the edge of the pool. There were plants floating on the surface of the water. Potting soil adhered to the side of the pool finish in thick stripes. A jumbled pile of dirt near the drain swayed back and forth in the water.

I took off my sandals and lowered my feet into the cool water, hoping to lessen the boiling temperature raging in my gut. With my back to Magic, I could hear him making a low guttural noise.

"Don't be mad."

I closed my eyes and counted to ten. *Lauren, let it go.* Hot breath set fire to the back of my right shoulder. A lick followed. I knocked my shoulder back, pushing him in the face so he would let me cool down on my own terms.

"Mission complete."

He put his muzzle under my elbow and flicked his head. My arm flung out to the side making just enough room for him to weasel his body next to mine. He leaned in and gave me an affectionate slurp on the side of my face. I grabbed his neck and pulled him in close, burying my face into his muzzle. "Why do I love you so much?"

A STORM IS A-BREWIN'

If my main objective in adopting another dog was to find a playmate for Maddie, I had indeed accomplished my task. The dynamics of how they played changed dramatically every few days but always included wrestling, chasing, and snarling. When they stood on their back legs and "bear wrestled," I was both amused and terrified, watching them duke it out like two prize fighters. I cringed as they nipped and swatted each other's limbs until one, knocked off balance, tumbled to the ground, bringing down everything in a six-foot radius.

On most occasions, Magic's invitation to play proved to be so irresistible that within minutes they were tangled up, swirling around in circles, gaining speed and force like a tropical disturbance that quickly escalated into a tropical storm. Their wrestling sessions had shockingly similar characteristics to historical events like Hurricane Dog, which in 1950 was named the most intense hurricane of the season. True fact!

Tropical storms are given a short, easily remembered name for the purpose of communicating and broadcasting information about them to the public. Each one is unique because of their characteristics and paths. I decided the fur buster storms blowing through our household needed a name, too. It seemed to be an excellent way to help recount the twisters in greater detail to my family and friends. The first storm was named Loco. It made landfall a month after Magic's adoption.

The calmness of the afternoon felt surreal following the prior four weeks of mayhem. The four-legged cyclones joined me in the family room, relaxed and content, enjoying the cool breeze blowing from the air conditioning vent. Maddie, looking more like a sphinx than a dog, watched Magic, sprawled on his back, shimmying back and forth on the area rug, flirting with her. I slumped back onto the couch, paging through a food magazine until I found the perfect recipe for a rich chocolate cake.

I disappeared into the garage to make sure there was a bottle of buttermilk crammed somewhere in our outside refrigerator. When I returned, Maddie walked toward the kitchen, but after she had taken only a few steps, Magic leaped up and intercepted her. He bumped her flank and bit the scruff of her neck. Maddie dipped her head to loosen his hold and then lunged forward, pasting her sturdy torso against his. She herded him like he was a lost sheep, forcing him to walk in circles. This gave Maddie the precise angle to lunge and grab his ear. With a firm hold, she proudly led him around. Magic, acting in defiance of her dominance, whipped his head from side to side, breaking her grip. Quickly, Magic jumped on her back, knocking her to the ground. Maddie let out a loud snarl and scrambled to her feet. Anticipating Maddie's counter attack, Magic reared up on his back feet and threw his front paws on the tile. Maddie roared, landing squarely on Magic's neck. Black and white fur blurred together until Magic freed himself from his entrapment. With a swift pivot of his body, he slammed into her chest. They both plummeted to the ground and rolled until they smashed into the couch.

"Hey, stop, stop. What are you guys doing?"

Unfazed, they clambered to their feet and charged each other in a game of chicken. When neither one altered their collision course, they met face to face, front paws waving wildly in the air, dancing on their back feet. Two seventy-pound masses of whirling fluff spun out of control, scattering everything. In a matter of moments, Tropical Storm Loco had left a trail of destruction and chaos in its wake.

I surveyed what was left of my carefully decorated family room and let out a wail. "You must be kidding me. Maaddiee! Maaagic!" Both dogs stopped in their tracks and dropped to the floor.

An antique lamp lay on its side, the shade torn in two places from colliding with a picture frame. The TV remote poked out from under the lampshade. A stack of books, swiped off the coffee table by forceful tails, lay in contorted positions. One book, upended on its spine, looked like an accordion with the pages flapping back and forth, as though desperately trying to find a resting place. Two couch pillows were jammed under a chair, their embroidered patterns slashed by razor-sharp toenails.

"Magic, you started this whole thing," I said, putting my hands on my hips.

"Didn't."

"You look guilty."

"Not the only dog in the room."

As I cleaned up the damage left in the wake of Loco, I made a mental note to pay more attention to the dogs' escalating level of play, and either break up the storm before it spiraled out of control or move out of its way.

The second storm, Jolt, taught me to think about planning an escape route in advance, but it also gave me my first lesson about what to do when an evacuation route was no longer an option. I named the exercise, Operation: Hunker Down.

That morning, Michael departed early for work after feeding the dogs. Tired from the weeks of interrupted sleep with Magic, I didn't set my alarm clock, hoping to grab a few more hours in precious dreamland. I didn't know where I got the delusional thought that I could sleep in until eight am, but it was a sure sign I was still suffering from the psychological effects of sleep deprivation. Thankfully, the bags under my eyes had started to shrink from the size of golf balls to grapes.

Magic and Maddie, with full tummies and no audience for their game, took their antics into a new arena: our bedroom. Charging through the door from the hall at the speed of light, they pounced on the bed, tackling each other and steamrolling me in the process. My peaceful dreams were interrupted by what can only be described as a furry cyclone blazing a trail down the middle of my bed. Trampled by multiple huge paws on my stomach, I let out a shout. Pillows and blankets flew in all directions. Magic misjudged the edge of the bed and crashed over the side, taking the alarm clock radio with him.

"Stop, stop!" I pleaded.

Maddie, close at Magic's heels, followed him, and with one tail sweep, created her own microburst. The lamp, magazine, and cream jar on the nightstand hit the floor. The lid came off the jar and large globs of white goo spattered the lamp shade and magazine cover. A glass of water collided with the wall and liquid trickled down the drywall in narrow lines. I bolted upright, panicked about what could happen next. I shot out of bed and chased tails, trying to maximize damage control, but the dogs thought we were playing a game of tag fueled by flying fur and scattered bed linens. I caught up to Magic and lunged for his collar but tripped over my nightgown and, with flailing arms, took a dive. Lying on the tile floor, I checked to see if all my limbs were still intact. Magic paused at my side and gently slurped my arm.

Dazed, I sat up and glared at Maddie and then at Magic, but the stare-down didn't last long. Magic sported a huge doggy grin, seemingly pleased to have brought me back to life. "Stop licking me," I muttered tersely.

"All better?"

When I stood to assess the damage, I wondered how many storms might be in my future. I flinched at the thought that the season might be just beginning.

I dug my way out of the newly leveled room, mopped up the water puddled by the baseboard, and cleaned off the areas smeared with night cream. I reasoned that stepping in to curb their romp left my health and general safety at risk. I vowed to be smart and stay out of the storm's route because trying to deflect it was meddling with

Mother Nature. How would I know when to clear the area if I didn't know another one was approaching? I couldn't turn on the television to receive updates about impending fur blaster storms. Nope. I had to pay closer attention and tune into what Maddie and Magic were doing.

The solution seemed so simple: be present. How difficult was it to be in the moment, not be distracted or thinking about something else while they were playing? Very difficult, I would soon learn.

A week later, consumed with my agenda of cleaning the house and creating a culinary masterpiece for a dinner party of eight, I failed to recognize that Storm Red, headed squarely in my direction, could have been avoided.

I worked the greater part of the morning preparing an Italian red sauce that Leonardo Da Vinci would have called a masterpiece. That afternoon I dusted, vacuumed and washed the floors, cleaned the kitchen, and buffed the quartz counter tops until they reflected the light from the ceiling fixtures.

When I heard dog yips brewing in the next room, it would have been the perfect time to transfer the cooled pasta sauce to the refrigerator and retreat from the area instead of admiring my sparkling kitchen and swooning over my sauce. I stirred the thick red gravy in a large, stainless steel bowl, adding the remaining spices and fresh basil. I had fussed and simmered the meat and wine-infused sauce for hours, coaxing out the complex, sweet notes of the tomatoes, yielding a culinary tour de force.

Engrossed in smelling the aroma wafting from the bowl, I paid little attention to the dogs yelping in our master bedroom until the faint, whining coyote sound grew louder and louder. Tropical Storm Red was making landfall and as the dogs swirled, charged, and thumped their way into the kitchen, the yips morphed into howls and growls.

Holding the wooden spoon and the bowl of sauce, I searched for the quickest exit but couldn't move fast enough. I scrambled to dodge the airborne dogs so as not to get trampled, but I couldn't quite clear them, and with one blow my knees buckled. I fell backwards; the spoon and bowl shot straight up into the air. As a law of science states, what goes up must come down, and a split second later the entire bowl of sauce drenched us. I landed on my butt, temporarily stunned at the turn of events. Magic's legs straddled my lap and Maddie's hips poked into my back. Her white coat was covered with thick blotches of sauce, making her look more like a spotted red leopard than a lab. The left side of Magic's head was saturated in sauce that slid down his ears and covered his chops. He wasted no time in quickly licking the meat clumps with wide slurps of his tongue. Maddie didn't know where to start her feast———licking me, the floor, or the bowl. The white cabinets, the unsealed travertine floor, and the yellow wall were spattered with red sauce.

"You two are killing me!"

Magic seemed pleased with the turn of events. *"Yummy."*

"Oh my gosh, what a mess, my sauce, the dinner group!" My splintered thoughts trailed off.

Pasta with red sauce would not be on that evening's menu.

Meticulously scrubbing the kitchen gave me plenty of time to recall when I had previously escaped a fur storm. I had simply opened the door to the patio when they came whirling through the kitchen. Once outside, the weather conditions changed and the tropical storm downgraded to a tropical depression, dissipating as fast as it had started.

Why hadn't I thought to open the patio door when Tropical Storm Red reeled into the kitchen? The destruction could have been avoided. I scolded myself for not taking steps to prevent the disaster. That day, I learned to be more tuned in and nimble when a storm was a-brewin'.

THE TRIAL

On the rare occasion that Maddie or anyone else put an end to playing, Magic resorted to more creative attention-seeking behaviors. One night, following several unsuccessful attempts to engage each family member in a game of tug of war, Magic disappeared into the master bedroom. I tip-toed to the doorway and watched as he rolled out his plan to raid the open bottom dresser drawer. He turned his nose sideways, wedging it into the space. With an arched neck he pried the drawer open and dove face down into the stash of socks. Pulling out a pair of athletic footwear, he paraded by me with his prize and then barked to punctuate his find. But his bark dislodged the socks from his mouth, causing them to fall to the floor. I burst out laughing watching him woof at the stockings and then toss them into the air. He had succeeded in fulfilling his mission. He had my attention. He bounded over, jumped on me, and licked my face.

"Let's play."

If socks were unavailable, he made his rounds throughout the house in search of other amusements. His list included television remotes, shoes, backpacks, wallets, money and cell phone——pretty much any item a family member valued. Anything left unattended on counters or the floor signaled the beginning of a new game.

To try and keep our mischief maker in check, we had one table he couldn't reach, and we piled it high with Magic's lost and found items. The collection usually included half-chewed but salvageable objects and lone shoes. We knew at least one shoe would be safe on the table while we tried to figure out what had happened to its mate.

The entire family was guilty of kicking off shoes under the table during mealtime, making them an easy target for Magic. While searching for any savory morsels on the floor that had escaped our plates, he would keep an eye out for an abandoned shoe. He'd emerge with the captured toy delicately hanging off a canine tooth, and with his head high in the air, ears forward, and tail pointed to the ceiling, he'd proudly march right by us, gloating, *"Look what I found."*

If I absent mindedly left my shoes somewhere in the house, the challenge was to remember where I had last seen them. But even if I returned to the spot I was sure I had left them, either one or both shoes would have magically disappeared. If I found one shoe, I could spend twenty minutes searching methodically under chairs, couches, and the surrounding area for its lost mate. I would eye Magic, who was mindlessly dozing on the area rug. He looked innocent, and without pieces of chewed leather or an abandoned strap left as evidence, I didn't have the proof to bring criminal charges against him.

My shoes were not the only ones disappearing. During the first few days of the shoe kidnappings, I was met with accusations. Charlie and Seth thought I had taken steps to put an end to shoes being left all over the house, probably stashing them in a garage closet. I pleaded not guilty and suggested the kids wear another of the five dozen pairs they owned.

Two days later, I was cleared of the allegations when Seth's favorite soccer cleats and the leather thongs Charlie just *had* to wear to a pool party vanished without a trace or my intervention. By the time one of Michael's dress shoes and my clogs disappeared, I knew there were grounds for a formal investigation.

To begin the inquiry, I left a sandal in the middle of the family room as bait and then slipped out the front door. I waited for several minutes and then sneaked around the back of the house, peering in the family room window.

I shook my head in amazement at our clever canine shoe-napper as he executed his plan. Our thief stalked the abandoned sandal, checking to see if anyone was watching. I quickly ducked my head and placed my sweaty hand across my mouth to stop the giggling. He seized the heel in his front incisors and trotted over to the base of the couch against the wall. In one short hop onto the couch, with the sandal dangling from his mouth, he leaned over the back edge of the couch and dropped it into the abyss. I felt exuberant. I had cracked the case.

Armed with the evidence needed to press charges, I ran into the house feeling like a detective with a search warrant. Magic sat frozen in the middle of the family room, ears pinned and eyes wide. I kneeled on the couch, reached over the back, and with two hands pulled the evidence from the hiding spot. I turned to face the thief and, with a flick of my wrist, chucked them in his direction. "Bad dog. I'm not happy with you. We've been looking for these all week. These are not yours." Magic rolled his ears back and then carefully stepped over the pile. He eyed the hallway, debating which way would yield the best exit.

As he trotted away, he yowled, *"But I only chewed one. It smelled soooo good. But not like chicken."*

When everyone came home that evening, I revealed Magic's secret hiding place where multiple sandals, sneakers, and dress shoes had been carefully wedged out of sight. I summoned Michael, Charlie, Seth, and our thief into the family room, directing Magic to his bed, which was covered in an array of the kidnapped items. He took one look at the pile and barked loudly enough to make the windows rattle. Like a guilty criminal waiting for a verdict, he panted and paced the family room floor, avoiding eye contact.

"Busted."

"This court will now come to order," I announced. "Magic, come. Magic, sit." Magic nervously licked the air then sat at my feet. His hunched torso made him look small and sheepish. For a moment I felt sorry for him, until the shoe pile caught my eye. "I, Lauren, the prosecutor in the case of The Family vs. the Shoe-napper, am ready to present the arguments. Magic, you, the accused, are standing trial for stealing and hiding the family's shoes. Do you have anything you would like to say in your defense?"

Magic ruefully looked at me and then the rest of the family. *"You left the shoes out."*

I addressed Charlie, Seth, and Michael. "Are there any comments from the jury at this time?"

"Yes," said Charlie. "My favorite sandal is chewed in two places. He's been living with us for two months and he's not getting any better about staying away from our stuff. I think he should be banished to the laundry room to serve time for this injustice."

The comment sounded harsh. I didn't want Magic to be locked away in a room forever. I looked at him as though a dagger had been thrown at my heart.

"You know, if we all did a better job of putting stuff away, we wouldn't be having this discussion," Michael said. "Magic isn't totally to blame."

With wide eyes, I said, "Dad's right. Let's be honest, we're all guilty of that." I paused for a moment. "Maybe we need to think about other ways to keep him from shoe-napping."

"Like what," Charlie asked.

"Well, we could give him extra attention and exercise. What if you took Magic out for a run instead of playing more rounds of video games? Last time I checked video games don't help with your conditioning for soccer."

"I guess you're right," Charlie said. "We all know how much Magic loves to run. I could probably get down to a seven-minute mile if I trained with him."

"I get your point, Mom," Seth added. "You're never happy if you think we're spending too much time on the computer." He thought for a second. "I guess the next thing you are going to say is that Magic's teaching us to be responsible for our stuff by hiding and chewing our shoes. Just kidding. I know if I kept my shoes in the closet these things wouldn't happen. But that won't stop him from chewing stuff! Who knows when that will end? He could be in his puppy stage for years."

Seeing my reaction, Charlie said, "I know how much you love him, Mom, but you do put up with a lot of shenanigans. Can't deny that."

I gave Charlie a blank stare. "Would anyone else like to speak?"

"One more thing," Seth added. "He still barks a lot. He's such a psycho." He pointed at Magic, where he lay licking the floor. "I don't think there's such a thing as a time-out when it comes to Magic. I say he loses couch privileges for a month. I'm going to hide his favorite Frisbee and let him search for it for days——that's only fair, right?"

"I think we're getting away from the issue at hand," I quickly interjected. The conversation was going south, so I turned to make eye contact with our shoe stealer. "Magic, stop licking." He dropped his head up and down, up and down, the exposed whites of his eyes popping into my view like a neon sign blinking on and off.

"Nervous."

"Okay then, guilty as charged for the crime of shoe-napping," I stated. "I'm charging the jury to weigh in on the sentence of three months without treats——a severe punishment, in my opinion." When he heard the word treat, he lunged forward, gently licking my arm as if trying to make a peace offering.

"No treats? Noooo!"

The jury, feeling sympathy toward the criminal, sentenced him to no treats for ten days and released him on supervised probation. Although he spent the remainder of his ten-day suspension on his best behavior, the jury felt certain this was one perpetrator they would see on the stand again, and again, and again.

After his brief brush with the law, Magic focused on eliminating items that might land him in hot water again. So instead of shoes or socks, he picked me to be his next object of interest. That changed my thinking that shoe-napping may not have been such an awful crime.

His methods of engaging me varied, but Magic's persistent pestering would finally break me down. His goal was to make sure I couldn't ignore his pleas.

"I'm bored. Need someone to play with."

Anything preventing me from focusing on him fell into the category of immediate dislike, but the one he loathed the most was the computer. His frustration began when I sat at the kitchen table, opened my laptop, and started working. The clever canine had a number of diversions he used to sabotage my concentration. If a piercing stare didn't work, Magic would simply up the ante and throw his paw over my arm.

"Pet me."

"Magic, stop. Go bother Dad. I'll pet you when I'm done with this email."

"I want to be petted now."

Predictably, Magic climbed up on the chair next to me, sat coyly, and watched with great interest until he could no longer stand being ignored.

"Magic, why are you licking me?"

"Bored."

"Stop it. You're bugging me."

"I'll stop if you pet me."

If he was unable to make eye contact, he'd reach out his paw just far enough to strike my left hand, dragging my fingertips off the keyboard. "Magic!"

"I'll settle for a scratch."

If pulling my hands from the keyboard didn't stop the typing, he'd cross over to my chair and squeeze in behind me, pushing my body up to the edge of the table. Sometimes he'd sit quietly with his muzzle resting on my shoulder. Other times, I could barely concentrate with his incessant licking and drooling alternated with bouts of panting, his hot breath torching my shoulder.

"Magic, down," I commanded. "I can't get anything done when you're bugging me." Magic jumped off the chair and sat at my feet.

"Good boy. I'm almost finished. When I'm done, we'll go out and play Frisbee."

"Frisbee? Now?"

"Can you wait just one more minute?"

"No!"

Magic, spying an abandoned shoe under the table, picked it up and sprinted to a nearby dog bed to chew on the laces.

"Magic, you're incorrigible and you have the patience of a gnat. Fine. I'll guess I'll have to finish this later," I said, closing the computer screen.

Each time this happened, Magic's persistence would inevitably win out and I would take a break from whatever I was doing. The email would have to wait and could wait. It was a reminder that I needed to get off my computer and put my phone on "do not disturb" so I could reboot and give my brain a rest. I gave in, and whether lavishing him with affection or engaging in a relentless game of Frisbee, I knew who benefited the most from the activity. Believe it or not, it was me. Magic reminded me to prioritize what was important in my life and push secondary tasks to the side so I could refresh, connect with friends, share more family time, or take Magic out for some playtime.

This message came through loud and clear from a dog who at one time was reduced to a number and expiration date. I hadn't expected there would be teachable lessons from Magic's tropical storms, nor did I think that presiding as a prosecutor in a shoe napping case or participating in an impromptu Frisbee outing could be so meaningful.

19

THE GREAT RAT CAPER

I learned shortly after adopting Magic that rats, rabbits, squirrels, and even coyotes were far more interesting to chase than the predictable soggy tennis ball bobbing in the pool or Frisbee whirling fifty yards down a golf course. Magic, by virtue of being a Labrador Retriever, had inbred traits of a natural born hunter and was eager to demonstrate his prowess whenever possible.

He possessed two important skills needed for a good hunting dog: a strong prey drive and the athleticism of a Navy Seal. Magic's persona changed when he was in hunt mode. His typically goofy smile and happy-go-lucky wiggle were abandoned. A single-minded beast emerged with tight lips, tensed torso muscles, laser-focused eyes, and arched tail pointing toward the sky. When the opportunity presented itself, he was ready for the challenge. Nothing broke his concentration, not even the temptation of a juicy steak within striking distance.

I surmised that Magic considered himself an excellent hunter, too, because he never missed an opportunity to demonstrate his skills.

Being a chef, I was thrilled to have lemons, limes, and three kinds of oranges outside the back door. There was no substitute for the fresh fruit and juices used in my recipes. Unfortunately, I wasn't the only one interested in the sweet flesh of the oranges. Roof rats found them delectable as well. How they migrated into our neighborhood is still a mystery despite reports they came as stow-a-ways on land-scaper's trucks.

With fruit trees abundant in every adjacent yard, it shouldn't have been a surprise when the hungry rodents set up camp on our roof to enjoy the smorgasbord of dangling fruit.

Roof rats are nocturnal. They leave a trail of hollowed-out orange globes to indicate their presence. They can squeeze through a hole the size of a quarter, so a house not tightly sealed can allow access through an open conduit or hole in the roof. We had no idea there was an uncapped, abandoned pipe that ran from the outside of the block wall into the interior of our bedroom. The pipe was large enough to roll out the welcome mat for a couple of the critters. We discovered the new guests had a late check-in one night after we had gone to sleep.

Magic, hogging up the biggest portion of the bed, had stretched out his legs against my side. I will never know whether it was a dream or a bout of restless leg syndrome, but multiple blows came from his direction. Sharp toenails jabbed my rib cage, jarring me awake. Star-tled, I lifted my head and gave our bed hog a stiff-armed push. Magic, feeling my forceful jolt, lifted his head off the mattress. Before settling back to a restful position, a muffled, slow scratching noise from inside the drywall caught his attention. He popped up like a jack-in-the-box. Hopping into a wide track stance, ears angled forward, he listened intently to sounds coming from behind the dresser. I shivered as a rush of anxiety spiked. I hoped it was the rustle of the wind brushing leaves against the house, but Magic knew it had nothing to do with wind. He flew off the bed and wedged his nose close to the baseboard, trying to pick up a scent. He snorted so loudly that I thought with the volume of air he was pushing in and out of his nostrils he would pass out from hyperventilating. Clawing to get behind the dresser, he whined, unable to make the cabinet budge.

"Something's in there. Hurry."

"Magic, stop barking. What are you doing?" I moaned.

"What, Magic? Why are you barking?" Michael sleepily called out.

"Navy Seal on duty." Magic raked his toenails across the baseboards and down the wall. Shreds of gypsum floated to the floor.

Michael rolled over. "Magic! Stop that. Now."

"Hon, I think there's something inside the wall. Magic's trying to find it but can't figure out how to get past the drywall."

"Magic, calm down!" Michael yelled over a continuous stream of barks.

I jumped out of bed, grabbed Magic by the collar and gave him a command to sit. He tried to jerk his way out of my hold.

"Can't sit."

"Wait a minute. It couldn't be those roof rats again? I hate those things."

Michael sat up. "Could be. But who needs a rat trap when you have a dog like Magic?"

"Is that supposed to make me feel better?" I said, turning off the light. "Oh my gosh, am I going to wake up and find a rat in our bed?"

"Not if I can help it."

"Let's not worry about it tonight. There's nothing we can do right now. The good news is that they're stuck behind the wall. I'll set a trap tomorrow. If you make an appointment with the exterminator, I'm sure they'll figure out how they got in."

I sighed. "I'll get on it right away."

Magic slept at the bottom of the mattress so he could keep one eye and ear open in case duty called. All was quiet. I wondered if Magic being on rat alert wasn't such a bad thing.

The next morning, I picked several dozen oranges for a recipe and placed them in a plastic bag, leaving them on the floor of the laundry room. I pulled the door shut to keep Magic from thinking they were orange-scented tennis balls. I should have guessed they wouldn't be of interest after finding him in the master bedroom staring at the previous night's crime scene. I patted Magic on the head. "Silly dog. Don't you know those yucky rodents are only active at night?"

"I can wait."

Magic dropped to the floor and pasted his nose to the baseboard, inhaling deeply. With a raised tail, he leaped to his feet, centering on all fours. His ears flicked back and forth; he looked right, then left.

"They're on the move." He charged out of the bedroom.

"Magic, where are you going?"

"Navy Seal mission."

"You are such a silly dog," I said, returning to the family room to complete the morning cleanup.

I stopped fluffing a pillow when I heard a banging noise and the shuffle of toenails in the kitchen.

"Magic, what are you doing?" I yelled. I had a scary flashback. How many times a day did I say that to our toddlers when they were out of sight, and I was unsure of what they were doing? No doubt, there was trouble brewing.

Seconds later, Magic darted over and nudged me in the elbow with his muzzle. His pupils danced from side to side. He panted and threw his head around like a wild horse. *"Rats. Hurry."*

"Magic, stop," I said, trying to ignore him and returning to fluff the rest of the pillows. Unable to snag my attention, he turned and sprinted back into the kitchen.

I heard a thud and a yelp as he slammed into something. Two seconds later, he bounded back into the family room. I tried to step out of the way, but two paws caught me dead center in the chest, pushing me backwards. I regained my balance and shoved his paws to the ground. He leaped into the air, barking so loudly I covered my ears.

"Come. Quick!"

"Why are you so fired up?"

Magic dashed back toward the kitchen. I followed him past the breakfast bar, sink, and range. He had stopped short at the door leading to the laundry room. Our Navy Seal, in a frenzy, hit the door with his paws trying to force it open. Panting heavily, his tongue zipped from side to side. His tail was as stiff as a lightning rod.

"Okay, Magic, hold on," I said, pulling him away from the door using every ounce of strength I could muster.

"I'll get 'em."

I opened the door a crack. He barged though the small space, charging into the room like a bull. With legs spread wide in attack mode, his eyes swept every inch of the space looking for clues. He pounced on the trash bag that had discarded bits and pieces of peels scattered by the dryer, nostrils flaring. I hesitantly entered the room and tiptoed over to the washer and dryer to get a better look. I pulled away the small trash can beside the dryer and crouched to peer behind the appliance, but I couldn't see anything.

"Let me see."

Magic took one giant leap, climbed up my back, and catapulted behind the dryer. The cramped space was not big enough for him to go forward or backward, so with his body pinned against the wall he did a reverse jump and slammed into me.

"Ahhhh!" I screamed. "Maaagic!"

Chaos erupted. Magic charged the front of the washing machine. A terrified rat scurried out from under the dryer, ran through my legs, and bolted across the floor, making a beeline for the door. My scream redirected Magic's attention. He spun around and hit the trash can, sending peels and dryer lint onto the floor. On high alert, with legs flailing in all directions, Magic cut off the rat's escape route and grabbed the rodent mid-scamper. He shook the fur ball with the ferocity of Attila the Hun. Our hunter raced through the open patio door, sprinted to the grass, and released the now motionless rat onto the ground.

"Told you I'd get it."

"Magic, that was amazing. Thanks for taking that yucky thing outside. Good job," I cheered, running my hand down his back.

The rats must have followed the scent that led them to a laundry room vent and then flattened into a pancake to push themselves through the grate and into the land of plenty.

"How about a treat?"

"Treat? Let's gooooo." Magic bolted back to the house and disappeared through the doorway. He was sitting in front of the pantry door when I entered the kitchen. *"What took you so long?"*

"Magic, I'm scared there might be another rat in the house. If there's one hiding somewhere, I sure hope Dad catches it tonight in a trap."

"No need with me around. Treat now?"

I pulled out his favorite chicken jerky strips and tossed one in the air. Magic caught the savory snack, swallowing it in one gulp. *"Yum."*

"Mission accomplished. Now, let's go brush those teeth."

Later that day an exterminator filled the holes and capped the abandoned pipe, ending the need for our hunter to be on patrol. But the heroic thrill of the Great Rat Caper left an indelible mark on our dog. If anyone said the word "rat" or "Magic, where's the rat?" he would spring into investigative mode with a rigid tail, flaring nostrils and fiery eyes. He'd stand with neck held high looking anxiously right and left, ready to continue the quest, resorting to frenzied barking mode to punctuate his determination.

"Navy Seal ready for action."

20

STINKPOT MAGIC

The Great Rat Caper was a prelude to the summer adventures that awaited Magic in the Flagstaff mountains. Every May, I opened up our cabin so when schedules permitted, anyone in the family could head north to escape the heat, and leave the desert city in the rear-view mirror.

Magic looked forward to his romps in the woods. A short, two-block walk from the cabin led us to the entrance of state game land I referred to as Magic's personal amusement park. When he saw the familiar dirt path, Magic tried to bust out of his harness. There were squirrels, jack rabbits, chipmunks, and deer, but his most favorite critter to find and wrangle was a skunk. Inevitably, Magic would see an animal and drag me several feet until I regained enough control of his antics to unbuckle the leash.

"It's a squirrel!" Magic raced down the hill in hot pursuit, jumped across rotted logs, and dove into patches of grasses, temporarily vanishing only to reappear in silence, like a panther stalking its prey. The squirrel, fearful that he might be an afternoon snack, detoured to the closest tree, scampered up to the highest limb, and chattered, scolding Magic for chasing him.

"Magic, come," I yelled, sprinting down the hill, but the hunter continued his pursuit running circles around the base of the tree.

"Game on." Magic backed up ten feet and charged the tree. With one jump, his momentum propelled him up the trunk. He dug his claws into the bark and pulled his body up in an attempt to reach the lower branches with his front paws. He was trying to shimmy up a tree!

"What are you doing?" I asked breathlessly, watching his paws slide down the trunk and shower his face with pieces of bark. "You're a silly dog. Don't you know dogs can't climb trees?"

"That's what you think."

"Geez, Magic. If you want to be off leash you have to come to me when I call you. Hey, are you listening to me?"

"Didn't catch the squirrel. Next time."

I reached out to snap on the leash, but he broke away from my grasp, taking two steps sideways and scanning the area. Holding his nose high in the air, only his nostrils twitched.

"Magic, what do you smell?" Was he breathing in the scent of decaying wood, earthy pine, and wildflowers? He lowered his head and pivoted his face toward me.

"Lunch."

Ready to continue his quest, he decided the surplus of hollowed out tree stumps would be his next area of interest. With his nose glued to the ground, he sniffed, inhaling deeply. Then he took off. Unable to keep up with his feverish pace, I walked behind him until the boom of barking broke the silence of the tranquil wilderness. Barking wasn't a good sign.

"Darn it, Magic," I muttered. I hastened my step in the direction of the ruckus until I arrived in a heavily wooded area, dark from the Ponderosas pines filtering out the sunlight. Downed tree limbs lay in contorted positions. Trying to maintain my balance amidst loose rocks and exposed roots presented a challenge.

Like a homing device, Magic had zeroed in on a decomposing tree stump stripped of layers of wood with sprouting turkey tail mushrooms. I could see a cloud of dirt and dust being hurled into the air as

Magic pawed and raked the ground, trying frantically to dig a hole at the base of the tree.

"Let me at it." Magic backed up two feet and, with one thunderous woof, engaged his hindquarters and rammed his chest into the base of the stump like a bulldozer. He backed away and waited. All was quiet, but amidst the silence an odor of rotting onions and burning rubber drifted into the air.

"Eww, smells like the Easter egg I found under the couch."

"No, Magic! It's a skunk. Treats, treats." I started running away in hopes he would follow. It was a fantasy to think that the great hunter on the verge of his second entrapment would have an interest in a treat, much less my sudden departure.

A black, triangular-shaped head with a white stripe running down its face popped over the edge of the stump. My worst nightmare stood on hind legs, propped his belly against the edge of the tree, and wildly waved his paws in the air, ready for a boxing match. Magic leaned in and snapped repeatedly at the swinging paws until the skunk's sharp claws caught the hunter's nose. Magic backed off with a yelp. Drops of blood spotted his muzzle.

"Yowl, arrrrrrouch."

"Magic, c'mon, boy. You're already hurt. Your nose is bleeding. Let me look at it."

"Not now."

The skunk, having set back his attacker temporarily, knew he had to find a more secure hiding place. He exited the tree stump and looked for a nearby fox hole. Despite his battle wound, Magic sprang into combat mode, ready to make his final move. The skunk stomped his foot, warning his perpetrator to stay away, but Magic was oblivious. As the Navy Seal closed in, the black and white bandit hunched up his back, folded into a u-shape, and lifted his tail.

"Magic! Get out the way, you're going to get——" A hurdling mass of pungent oil sprayed his face and neck. In shock, Magic dropped to the ground and rolled in the dirt, trying to rub off the eye stinging grease.

"Can't see."

"Oh, Magic. You poor dog. Are you alright?" As Magic made swipes to rid his face of the burning substance, I held my nose, leaned in, and snapped on the leash. But before I could clear the area, I saw Magic winding up for a full body shake.

"Noooo!" I screamed, but it was too late. I watched his loose skin whip from side to side, spinning dirt, oil and blood onto my body. "Magic, that was not a good dog."

Grabbing my t-shirt to show him, I said, "See what happens when you go after a skunk? I'm not happy with you right now."

Magic looked over at me with a sheepish grin. *"Sorry."*

I took a big breath and looked closer at the splotches of musk oil that had formed rings around Magic's eyes. "You look like a raccoon, I look like a Dalmatian, and we both smell like a skunk. Great duo we are. Let's go home and get a bath."

"No, you take a bath."

We jogged back to find Maddie and Michael making their way down the trail.

"Let me guess." Michael pinched his nose, speaking like Porky the Pig. "Smells like an angry skunk to me," he said, moving a cautionary distance from the two of us. "C'mon, Maddie girl, looks like your walk is being cut short today. We need to get back to the cabin before the stink squad arrives."

Michael turned to me. "Let me get a head start, please." He tightened up Maddie's leash and picked up his pace in hopes of staving off cross-contamination.

I turned and scowled at Magic. "Hey, thanks to your skunk adventure, Dad and Maddie want nothing to do with us. Do you know why? Because they don't want to smell like rotten eggs, too. You're just going to have to wait ten minutes until they get back to the cabin. Magic, sit." Magic, no longer the leader of the pack, barked in defiance as his two comrades disappeared down the path.

"Don't want to sit."

He panted, whimpering quietly. I pulled out my phone and dialed my friend Suzy to ask about the virtues of tomato juice as an anti-skunk treatment. The call went to voicemail.

"Hey Suzy, I know your dog Sweet Pea got skunked last year. Did you use tomato juice? Just wondering what to do. I'm sure you're shocked that Magic got sprayed. What a mess. We'll be cleaning up for days. Call me when you get a chance. Thanks."

As I stared out into the forest, waiting for Suzy to call me back, Magic shot up from a sitting position like he had been bitten by a horde of fire ants. He spun in tight circles, twisting the leash and tangling up his hind legs. I dropped my end of the leash and reached down to untangle the mess, but Magic, seeing he was temporarily untethered, jumped into the air. With legs freed he reared back, clocked me in the head, and threw his weight forward. I was too busy bracing for a face plant into the dirt to try and chase him. With the leash bumping along the trail, Magic raced down the path looking for Michael and Maddie.

Michael heard the sound of pounding feet and turned, expecting to see a herd of deer, but instead saw Magic barreling straight for Maddie.

"Magic!" Michael blurted out. "Get off her. Noooo… you're getting that skunk stuff all over her. Stop."

Michael grabbed Magic's collar and pulled him away from Maddie's back. "Geez, Magic, now you've really done it. All of us stink."

"I'm the leader. If leader stinks, everyone stinks."

I could hear Michael yelling. It was not joyful. I limped to the trail entrance, dusting off clumps of dirt.

"What in the heck just happened? I thought you were going to wait until Maddie and I got home."

"I tried to, but he got away from me," I said defensively. "Sorry." Looking at my husband glaring at me, I couldn't stop grinning. "It could be worse."

"I don't think so."

"Could be roof rats in our bed," I said.

We both laughed.

"Okay, Magic, you've caused enough trouble for one day. Come here." I reached over and grabbed the leash.

Michael was silent for a minute as we walked to the cabin. "I don't want these dogs inside," he finally said. "Let's tie them to the fence while we prepare for bath battle."

"Okay, and just to let you know, I called Suzy to ask about using tomato juice, but I haven't heard back from her yet."

"Do we even have tomato juice?"

"We have Bloody Mary mix."

Michael rolled his eyes as he secured the dog's leashes to the fence. He disappeared into the garage to find a bucket and stack of towels while I gathered up the bath supplies. As I rounded the corner of the bathroom and walked into the family room, there was Magic with wide eyes and ears pricked forward.

"No, Magic, no! Not the carpet." He dropped to the floor, rolled on his back and splayed his legs in opposite directions. Hearing my scream, Michael came charging through the garage door and into the family room. Magic jumped up on all fours and assumed a wide track stance looking ready for a football tackle. Michael dove in to grab the leash but missed. Magic pressed his face onto the area rug, and with dropped knees and torso high in the air, scooted his muzzle down the length of the rug like a snowplow.

"That felt good."

"Magic, no," I said, snaring the leash. "What are you doing in here? Oh my gosh, you reek and now the rug and cabin do, too. This is unbelievable. Michael, I thought you tied him to the fence."

"I did. I have no idea how he got away."

"You smell, too. Maybe you should be tied to the fence."

I took a deep breath and led Magic to the deck. As he walked across the outdoor rugs, he whipped his head sideways, pulled away from my grip, and crashed onto the rug. His rolled on his back, thrashing legs high into the air with lightning speed as if he was trying to suppress the irritation of one hundred mosquito bites.

"Scratch, please. Hurry."

The rotten egg smell permeated everything, both inside and out, making it impossible to breathe without wincing. With Magic and Maddie securely tied to the fence, I went inside to retrieve the shampoo, conditioner, and bucket that were strewn around the family room. Michael collected the towels and extended the hose twenty feet from the cabin for the decontamination zone.

Thus, the bathing process began. The water that came out of the ground in Flagstaff was cold in mid-July. I turned the faucet to the shower setting and let the water run down Magic's face but noticed something odd happening. The force of the water was moving the oil slick down his back. I cringed, watching globules of oil absorb into his fur. Why did I think hosing him down with water was the right approach? I knew oil and water don't mix.

Magic backed away. *"Don't like cold water."*

"What's your problem, Magic? You like baths."

His eyes narrowed. *"Never said that."*

"I know the water is a little chilly, but retrievers aren't supposed to be affected by cold water," I said to Magic. "You're bred to fetch waterfowl out of ponds in icy temperatures."

"What? You're calling me average?" Magic's reluctance to retrieve the ball out of the pool if the water dipped below eighty-five degrees should have alerted me there was a problem.

The next eight baths were challenging as Magic tried to escape the repeated dousings of water. We became frustrated because he still smelled like skunk.

He barely made an attempt to shake off the water. *"Cold, cold, cold."*

His beautiful radiant coat, stripped of natural oils, looked dull and coarse. Defeated, he curled up into a ball on the grass. I assembled a nest of clean towels and called him. Magic hesitantly stood, limped over, and slowly lowered his body onto the nest. I snapped on his leash and looped it around the fence post. "I'm sorry, Magic, but maybe this will teach you not to mess with a skunk."

"Not today. Maybe tomorrow."

I turned to Michael. "So how are we going to deal with the horrible stench in the cabin? I think we should take a break and talk about what to do next."

We dried off and walked inside. Sipping on a glass of water, I reached over, opened the computer, and typed in the word "skunked."

"Oh honey," I moaned to Michael. "Why didn't we take the time to read about the antidote to skunk spray? We did everything wrong."

"Do I really want to hear this?"

"We should have first blotted the excess oil off with a paper towel and then combined baking soda, hydrogen peroxide, and dishwashing soap as an elixir and worked that into his coat. Oh, and all clothes, collars, and harnesses need to be soaked in that same solution before going into the washing machine."

"Can I leave now?" Michael asked.

Slamming the computer shut, I ran into the kitchen. Rummaging through the pantry I found half of box of baking soda and held it up for Michael to take a look. "I might have a little hydrogen peroxide under the sink, but not enough. Would you drive to town and buy several quarts of hydrogen peroxide and three boxes of baking soda?"

"I'm going to need more than that," Michael said, placing his water glass in the sink. "I'll need a couple six packs, too. Give me a few minutes to change clothes. The car is the only thing that doesn't smell like skunk right now. That may be a sleeping option for you tonight."

With a scowl, I said, "Easy for you to say. You're headed back to the valley tonight to the skunk free zone. Good thing the boys weren't here this weekend. I don't think they would have liked being in the middle of this mess."

"You got that right!"

When Michael disappeared into the bedroom, I put on my chef hat, hoping to come up with a plan to counter the odor in the cabin. Boiling vinegar was an option, but I didn't want to replace one stinky smell with another one. *Ohhh, I know the one aroma nobody in the family can resist. The scent of freshly baked cinnamon buns, of course. I may not be able to whip up a dozen in the next twenty minutes but replicating the smell is a no-brainer for a chef.*

I set the oven temperature to two hundred fifty degrees, pulled ground cinnamon from the pantry, and sprinkled half of the bottle onto a baking sheet. I was placing the pan in the oven when Michael entered the kitchen with clean clothes.

"I wasn't sure what to do with my dirty clothes, so I left them in the shower."

"No worries, I'll make up a batch of the skunk elixir when you come back and give them a good soak. On the bright side, what else could go wrong today? Things have to get better from here."

"Let's hope so. I'll be right back." Michael gave me a wink and headed for the door.

I poured baking soda into a wire sieve and sifted the powdery substance over every inch of the rug like I was dusting Christmas cookies with confectionary sugar. When the sweet spice wafting from the oven started to perfume the air, I turned it off. My idea to mask the stench had worked.

The rug was ready to be vacuumed. I pulled the sweeper from the closet and cleared the mounds of baking soda when the sound of frantic barking erupted over the roar of the vacuum. Hoping it was not another skunk encounter, I raced to the deck.

There they were in the yard. A handful of Martian-like people covered from head to toe in white hazmat suits were wrapping the edge of our property in plastic tape. They had secured trees, our mailbox, and the side yard fence in one long loop of yellow caution tape. People in cars stopped to take a look at what was going on. Neighbors walked over to the adjacent street, thinking they were the first witnesses to a chemical disaster. I could feel the color drain out of my face. I scanned the front yard, looking for signs of carnage. Was there an accident? Who were the people traversing our yard and unreeling more and more tape? Were they police? Firemen?

"Hey, what's going on here?" I called out. "What are you doing?"

Nobody answered. Magic and Maddie repeatedly lunged to break loose from the fence.

"Navy Seal ready for duty."

I bolted across the deck and jumped down the steps two at a time to reach the dogs, holding them firmly by their collars.

I frantically yelled, "Would somebody please tell me what's happening?"

The masked perpetrators pulled off their face coverings to reveal

Suzy and other friends of ours who had decided our situation was the perfect set-up for a prank. After listening to my voicemail about using tomato juice to combat a skunk attack, she must have contacted our buddies and told them what happened. I untied Magic and Maddie and walked them up the stairs into the cabin. After shooing them into the garage, I walked out to the edge of the deck, slamming the patio door behind me. I surveyed the cast of characters laughing in the yard as Michael pulled up. He slowly drove the car into the driveway, maneuvering through the people who had congregated around the cabin. Michael rolled down his window and shot me a look of concern. Seeing his chin drawn back and eyes wide, I knew he was freaked out, too. He got out of the car, sprinted up the deck stairs, and grabbed my shoulder.

"What in the heck happened while I was gone? Did something blow up?"

"Apparently, our friends, the ones you see out there dressed in hazmat suits, thought it would be entertaining to alert the entire neighborhood that we got skunked."

"Not funny," Michael muttered. "Maybe we should ask those friends of ours in their chemical warfare suits to help us clean up."

"Something tells me we won't have any takers," I replied. Their practical joke was less amusing in the wake of the work we had ahead of us. I was afraid if I said something it would not be friendly.

We spent the next five hours scrubbing, cleaning, and laboriously applying rounds of the miracle de-skunk elixir. At six o'clock, when Michael and I sat down for dinner, we clinked beer glasses, celebrating the skunk saga was over. But that celebration didn't last for more than a week. Magic would never grasp the concept that pursuing a skunk wasn't in his best interest. Because not once, not twice, nor the four times he fell victim to the stinky consequences of tangling with the rogue mammal could dissuade him from giving it one more go.

TALE OF THE TAIL

After dinner, Michael packed up and headed back to the valley to join Charlie and Seth, who had decided not to come up for the weekend. Normally I didn't look forward to our family's Sunday departures, but this was one night when the thought of being alone for a hot bath, mindless television, and a good night's sleep made me deliriously happy. There was only one more responsibility in the way of my self-indulgent activities: feed the dogs. Images of a deep tub with steaming water floated in my mind as I dreamily picked up dog bowls and retreated to the garage to fill their dishes. Exiting the garage with their kibble, I expected to see Magic leaping into the air and doing his normal three hundred and sixty degree turns in celebration of dinner. This time, only Maddie greeted me with a wagging tail.

"Maddie, where's your buddy?" I asked. Maddie gave a yip and ran down the hallway. I followed her into the kitchen. "Maddie, sit. Okay," I said, lowering her bowl to the floor.

I turned to look for Magic. With uncharacteristic calm, he stood by his water dish. "Mmmm, dinner. Magic, sit," I said, walking over and placing the bowl down. He lowered his hindquarters to the floor and let out a shrill whine before popping back on four feet. With pinned back ears, he stood motionless, waiting for the okay command to commence eating.

"Can't sit. Tail hurts."

"Okay, Magic, you don't need to sit."

After Magic finished his meal, he showed no sign of interest in an evening walk. Instead, he restlessly licked his lips, one minute burying his head in my lap, the next minute pacing and panting. Magic meandered around the family room, stopping briefly in front me, his eyes anxious and searching. I felt helpless. I didn't know what was happening. He circled the room three more times before melting onto the floor. Unable to get comfortable in any position, he winced in pain, jumping into a standing position. His paws remained glued to the floor.

I walked over and sat in front of him. "What's the matter, Magic?" I crooned. "Are you a-hurtin', boy?" The familiar thwack of his tail was eerily absent. I needed to figure out what was going on.

"Could this have something to do with what happened today? Let me take a look at you." I examined his paws, head, and legs, finding nothing unusual. But as I slid my hand over the end of his torso, he whimpered. To complete the inspection, I scooted around to his backside, catching full sight of Magic's swollen tail, the size of a Polish sausage.

"Magic, sweet boy, what happened to your tail? Is that why you're whimpering?"

I didn't know what caused the ailment but thought it might be an allergic reaction to the skunk oil. The condition looked serious and his steady whines fueled my insecurity about what to do next. An all too familiar feeling of doom loomed. I contemplated what might have caused the swelling. I worried that other parts of his body might be affected next. Magic could barely move his freakishly large tail and I feared the worst, convinced he could go into shock and die.

I reached for the computer and searched the internet using the key words "enlarged dog tail" and within minutes found an answer. Magic had a condition called limber tail, also known as broken wag, most often seen in retrievers or hunting dogs that have been exposed to frigid water or have had extended physical activity. The inflammatory response to the cold water causes the muscles to swell, causing pain and tenderness for three to five days. Three to five days! How was I going to play nursemaid to a dog that smelled like a skunk and couldn't go the bathroom, lie down, or sleep without wincing in pain? I shut the computer down and shuffled over to him. His glassy eyes held my gaze for ten seconds before breaking away.

"I'm so sorry for causing your limber tail. I feel terrible that you're in pain."

"Limber what?"

Despite the relief of knowing the condition wasn't life threatening, I chastised myself for subjecting him to repeated cold water baths. With the vet's office closed and only the internet to advise me on treatment options, I decided to wait until morning to consult our vet. Any fantasies I had about a good night's sleep were abandoned.

Magic's inability to find a comfortable resting position for the next three hours was difficult to watch. I turned on the television, hoping the distraction would give me an emotional break. When that didn't work, I reached for a book, but the story didn't hold my interest. All I wanted to do was stare at Magic, hoping to witness a miraculous recovery. I thought of the nights lying awake at Charlie and Seth's side when they were sick infants, willing their recovery through my intense love for them. I was a good mother to my kids, but was I being a good dog mom? I had my doubts.

Magic's puppy eyes beckoned my attention. He laid on his side, peering out the sliding glass window, watching squirrels scamper up tree branches and dogs trot by on the road. Nothing sparked his interest until I knelt beside him and gently stroked his ears. We melted together with unspoken compassion.

By nine-thirty, I was ready to turn in for the night, hoping the skunk adventure had come to an end. I helped Magic down the steps so he could make one last potty run. I let out a sigh of relief when he successfully peed in the yard. On the way into the cabin, I grabbed an old foam cushion from our deck furniture and bribed him to follow me with a treat into the bedroom. Magic watched me place the pillow on the floor.

"That's where you're sleeping tonight."

"Fat chance."

I pointed to the cushion on the floor. "Magic, go." Unenthusiastically, he stepped onto the make-shift dog bed and waited for a treat.

"Good dog," I said, tossing a jerky strip. "You need to sleep there tonight because I don't want a dog and a skunk to be bunking with me. Why can't you be like Maddie and sleep on the floor for one night? I got you a comfy pillow."

"Doesn't feel comfy."

While washing my face and brushing teeth, I intermittently peeked my head around the bathroom door to check on Magic. "That's a good dog. Stay on your cushion."

"Not my cushion, remember?"

I disappeared into the closet and changed into pj's. The thought of climbing into bed and being engulfed under a cool set of sheets made me dance down the hallway and dive onto the mattress. I fluffed up the feather pillow, turned out the light and prayed for a restful night.

When a waft of sulfur filled the air, I knew Magic couldn't be too far away. Opening my eyes, I could barely make out the shape of his head resting on the edge of the mattress.

"Magic, what are you doing?" I turned on the light, reached over, and gave him a couple pats on his head. "I'm so tired. Aren't you ready to sleep after what happened today?"

"No. Tail hurts."

"Is your tail hurting? I'm sorry." I turned off the light, rolled over on my back, and breathed deeply, hoping he would think I was asleep. A wet nose nudged my exposed arm, and then pushed into my bicep to herd me into a new position. I didn't stir. Even my arm, wet with nose goo, remained still.

The high-pitched yowl was the only warning I received before Stinkpot Magic pushed off his back legs and landed in a heap in the middle of my stomach. Clamoring to take pressure off his sausage tail, he stretched out his front paws by my shoulders and straddled his back legs outside my thighs. I turned on the light to see a sphinx dog staring me in the face.

"What are you doing on top of me?" I gasped. "You're not sleeping in this bed tonight."

"Yes, I am."

Magic had made up his mind; he wanted comfort. No deck cushion on the planet or Florence Nightingale impersonator could make him feel better. He had to be close to me.

"Darn it," I said, hopping out of bed and heading toward the closet. I found an old comforter that could be sacrificed for the cause. "You need to move so I can cover the sheets." He dragged his body to the end of the bed and waited for me to smooth out the coverlet.

"You're all set. Now, let's get some sleep," I said, crawling under the covers. I sank onto the mattress and slipped into a peaceful state. Minutes later, a tug of the comforter alerted me that Magic was crab-crawling up the side of the bed.

"What are you doing now?" I asked impatiently.

"Can't sleep. Tail hurts."

"Would you stop moving around?"

"Can't."

He contorted his body into a number of positions but couldn't find one that made him comfortable. His chest squirmed and his paws fidgeted. He spun around in circles until losing control, collapsing on my stomach. He jumped on the opportunity to seize my full attention by giving me a huge slurp that covered my entire face.

"Magic, no licking. Even your breath smells like skunk."

"Pet me."

"Calm down," I snapped. "If you calm down, I'll give you a tummy rub, but only for a couple minutes."

By morning, we were both exhausted. The skunk smell had begun to dissipate, but Stinkpot Magic was reminded of the incident every time he tried to sit. His tail shrunk after two days with daily doses of aspirin.

Now we always keep aspirin and skunk elixir kits stashed under our bathroom sinks and in the garage. We may not be able to stop Magic from being sprayed but when he does at least we're able to take the stink away.

22

PARENTING: INSTRUCTIONS NOT INCLUDED

Navigating the waters of raising children starts from the moment they are born. Dependent on us from the first time we laid eyes on them, no amount of preparation could offset the distress Michael and I felt caring for a crying infant. Charlie had a dry diaper, so maybe he was hungry? No, he had been fed half an hour ago. Sick? Did I need to call a doctor? How could the hospital release a newborn to parents who didn't know what to do for a crying baby? That night, we saw the sun set and, bleary eyed, watched it rise the next morning. Looking back now, caring for Charlie was straightforward, requiring simple fixes. But as the kids grew up, our parental decisions became a lot more complicated. We stressed over what we should do, afraid our bad judgment could impact them for the rest of their lives.

Michael and I talked about issues like keeping them safe, building self-esteem, and finding the right medical treatments. But one of the most challenging topics we discussed was our inability to rein in our energetic boys. It didn't take me long to figure out Charlie and Seth had more energy at two and three than most kids their age. As toddlers, their daily activities started at six-thirty in the morning and continued until seventy-thirty at night. Other than a one-hour nap in the morning and afternoon, they were bodies in motion. An outing to the park, excursions with playgroup friends, swimming, playing with toys, dancing, and inventing a new game could all be jammed into a twelve-hour day. The house was in a constant state of disarray as they moved seamlessly from one activity to the next. I routinely found colorful Duplo blocks in planters and Matchbox cars strewn under chairs or other assorted places, such as the toilet. The orange and blue basketball hoop and play kitchen took up one wall of the family room, and the train set with miles of track looped around the couch.

Although I considered taking some time for myself during their naps, that never seemed to materialize. There were house projects to be attended to, like scheduling the plumber to get the Matchbox toy out of the clogged toilet while I prepped dinner. In the evening, Michael and I focused on dinner, baths, and bedtime stories. By the time the boys were tucked in, I was ready to enjoy a peaceful household, relishing the opportunity to read or talk to Michael without multiple interruptions. I'd try to stay awake but could barely make it fifteen minutes before dozing on the couch, exhausted from the day's activities. I accepted the boys' feverish pace and zest for all things in life as normal for active boys. I was pretty sure that wasn't ever going to change.

By the time they reached school age, they were ready to dive into a new experience. However, the school environment posed a challenge. They didn't fall into the spectrum of normal behavior, largely due to their unharnessed energy. Charlie had a hard time sitting still, and Seth was easily distracted by friends. Even though they both excelled academically, Charlie thought the classroom day was long and Seth had a hard time settling down to do homework after school.

I successfully dodged the dreaded conversation about attention deficit disorder until they entered high school. The suggestion from a guidance counselor that I have them evaluated came as no surprise. She gave me the contact information for a psychiatrist in the valley.

After Charlie and Seth were tested, the psychiatrist informed me the boys were on the cusp of having attention deficit disorder because they had some of the symptoms. The doctor felt that even though they couldn't be clinically diagnosed with the condition, they might benefit from medication. I knew Charlie and Seth were high energy and could be inattentive at times, but I thought all kids were under certain circumstances. Medication could help them concentrate in school, but they were doing well scholastically.

I thought back to my teens when I had an excessive amount of energy to burn and trouble focusing at times. My parents didn't have me tested because I don't think there was an awareness of ADD until the nineteen nineties. Fortunately, my mom and dad encouraged me to play a number of different sports and spent hours supporting my various hobbies to help me concentrate. Looking back, I was thankful they alleviated my issue with activities instead of medication.

Maybe that explained why, despite feeling pressure to follow through with the psychiatrist's recommendation to medicate the kids, my gut reaction told me it wasn't the right thing to do. But not taking the doctor's advice worried me. I had consulted him for his professional opinion and then chosen not to listen to him. How could I justify my judgment of the situation over a medical doctor's assessment? Simple: mother's intuition. I knew Charlie and Seth's personalities and character traits better than anyone.

I learned how to manage Charlie and Seth's behaviors just like my parents had for me. I read books on attention deficit disorder and talked to other mothers facing the same challenge. Armed with that information, I helped the kids manage the times they felt distracted and hyper. Being able to channel their physical and mental energy, they became leaders. Charlie and Seth played club and school soccer, which helped them to redirect their energy onto the sports field. They excelled in school and sports in the years that followed. The subject of ADD was never discussed again. I had no idea the kids encounter with the psychiatrist would give me the courage to take a stand for Magic at a veterinary appointment.

Several months after Magic's adoption, Charlie and Seth started making jokes about his endless bouts of farting and burping. There were numerous times when I frantically fanned the area with my hand while making an apology to guests, suggesting we move away from the stink zone. He tooted loud ones that couldn't be ignored, even by the perpetrator. A dog's sense of smell is supposedly one hundred times stronger than humans. He must have thought he was being held captive in an out-house.

He'd look around and cock his head as if questioning where the sound of the deflating balloon came from. But the tooting was the least offensive part of his flatulence. When the gaseous fumes wafted into the air, there would be a mass exodus shortly thereafter to escape the stench.

When gas didn't explode out of his tailpipe, sometimes air took a different route, forced out of his stomach, traveling up the esophagus, and settling into his mouth. I could see the burp coming. He'd extend his neck, open his mouth, and expel air with a gurgling crescendo as loud as a three-hundred-pound guy drinking beer at a frat party.

However, after a full year of mounting complaints and Seth suggesting Magic be relegated to the bathroom, permanently, I reluctantly made an appointment with a veterinarian. I dreaded the thought of taking him to a clinic, worried the familiar smells and restlessness of other dogs in the waiting room would trigger the behavioral issues we were working hard to overcome. How could I blame him for feeling that way? The environment reminded him of the time he spent at the city shelter and neuter facility. So, on the morning of the appointment, I gave him a bone to chomp on and a long Frisbee session to ease his anxiety. Looking back, I could have benefited from gnawing on a bone, too.

Magic sensed my frazzled nerves as I struggled to secure his harness. Why couldn't I buckle the clasp? How many times had I fastened the thing since his adoption? Five hundred? Seemed like more. Grabbing my purse, we headed to the car. Magic pulled on the leash, thunderously barking.

"Where are we going?"

"Magic, stop barking."

"Where's my frisbee?"

"Get in the car." I opened the door and watched him catapult into the back seat. "We aren't going anywhere until I get you buckled in. Magic, sit," I commanded.

"Can't sit. Too excited."

I strong-armed his body into position and attached his harness to the seat belt. "Okay, we're finally ready to go."

"What took you so long?"

I turned up the radio and sped toward the clinic. After I parked the car, and freed him from the restraint, he tore back and forth across the seat, peering out the windows.

"No grass? Not good."

He jumped into the cargo area and stood there, keeping his legs in a wide stance. I slowly opened the hatch, preparing for a full-blown escape attempt. To stop him from jumping out, I reached through the gap and grabbed his leash. As the door sprang open, Magic almost banged his head as he leaped out of the car. I experienced minor neck trauma as he bolted over to the nearest bush, manically sniffing multiple areas before peeing.

"Sorry. Nervous."

I directed him toward the entrance of the building, but his high-pitched bark and repeated hops into the air worried me so much that I considered scrapping the appointment. Magic's erratic behavior and the fact that it's never good news when you have to see a vet didn't help either. The twenty-five-dollar cancellation fee kept me moving forward.

I gathered the leash, choking up on the harness, and opened the door with one hand. Unable to contain himself, Magic barged into the clinic, sparking off three dogs to bark erratically. Embarrassed, I looked away from the other patients, limped over to the reception desk, and checked in with Shelly, the green-eyed vet tech.

Magic surveyed the room. *"Don't like this place."*

I looked him in the eye and said, "It's okay. Stop barking."

"Can't."

I took a seat in the waiting room, but Magic wanted no part of sitting. His eyes bulged and his mouth opened. Panting followed. I searched for a paper towel dispenser to mop up the saliva pooling on the tile floor.

Shelly watched as Magic anxiously paced to the end of his leash and then let out a yowl. I tugged him back, wrapping my hands around his belly. I bent down and whispered in his ear to calm down. When I lifted my head, I noticed people were glaring at us. I looked away, not wanting to meet their eyes. Being unable to control my dog was embarrassing.

I think Shelly felt sorry for us, because she walked over and asked me to follow her. Walking down the hallway, Magic's wild barks lifted his feet off the ground.

"Magic, stop." I said firmly.

"Okay, but this place stinks." We walked quietly the rest of the way to the exam room. I looked down at him with amazement that he had listened.

"The doctor will be with you soon," Shelly said.

"Thank you for getting us out of the waiting room. Magic gets crazy in vet offices. He's a rescue, you know..." My voice trailed off. What a weak excuse.

Magic, feeling trapped, traced a repeated path across the tiled floor. The only diversion was a faint bark coming from the hallway. He rushed to the door, pasted his nose to the jamb, careened his body sideways, and pawed the door with forceful jabs.

"Hey, it's okay, boy."

"Don't believe you."

Telling him everything was okay couldn't have been further from the truth. I bit my nails. My mouth dried up. How long did we have to wait? It seemed like an eternity before I heard a knock at the door.

Dr. Silvan, a middle-aged woman with piercing hazel eyes, entered the room. Her rigid posture and curt introduction made me uncomfortable. Magic, sensing my apprehension, shook with nerves. He refused to stand still during the exam and howled like a coyote. Like a mother attempting to coax her child to cooperate at a doctor's appointment, I tried to intervene and contain his behavior.

"Magic, sit."

"Don't want to."

"Magic, down."

Magic dropped to the floor, excessively licking the tile and then popped back up and barked. Loudly.

"She makes me nervous."

Dr. Silvan turned to me with a furrowed brow. "Lauren," she announced like she was delivering the verdict at a jury trial, "Magic is exhibiting mental and emotional issues."

"What?" I stared at her blankly, not knowing how to respond. I collected my thoughts.

"Dr. Silvan," I addressed her in the same tone she had spoken to me, "I didn't come here today to discuss behavioral issues you may think he has. I made the appointment to find out why he is farting and belching. I'm aware he's a little high strung but he's a rescue and sometimes rescues have baggage."

Dr. Silvan gave me a stone face as she scribbled some notes on a chart. "I need to obtain a good x-ray of Magic's esophagus and stomach cavity to address the problems you're talking about. But because of Magic's hyperactivity, we'll need to administer a sedative."

"You aren't going to put him out completely?" I asked. I could feel my throat burning.

"No. We'll reverse the sedative after the films are taken. He'll be groggy, but he won't be under full anesthesia."

I think she was irritated by Magic's tics and the fact that he wouldn't settle down. My anger mounted as she continued to interact with Magic in a dismissive way. The vet sighed multiple times in disgust. Dr. Silvan's inability to show any empathy toward Magic, knowing he had been granted a second chance at life, baffled me. Didn't she understand his behavior and fear responses were symptomatic of his past experiences?

"So, you're okay with us taking films?"

"Yes," I said begrudgingly.

Dr. Silvan abruptly turned and exited the room. A few minutes later, Shelly coaxed him to follow her into the hall. The exposed whites of his eyes etched a pitiful image in my mind. After the door shut, I felt despondent, realizing his complex emotional issues in addition to his physical ailments could be more serious than I anticipated. I feared what they might find on the x-rays. Maybe he'd be diagnosed with a condition that had severe long-term consequences or required surgery. I rocked back and forth on the chair to regain my composure.

Thirty minutes later, still waiting in the exam room, Shelly appeared at the door with Magic. His eyes were listless, his tail drooping. He staggered over to me, still heavily sedated, and collapsed on the floor. Shelly explained the drug would take some time to wear off and that we couldn't leave until he was alert. I sat on the floor, picked up his heavy head, and gently rolled it onto my lap. I stroked his velvety ears. Tears ran down my face and onto his muzzle where they sat like glass beads.

Our quiet moment was interrupted when Dr. Silvan entered the room and placed the films on the light box. Magic barely acknowledged anyone had come in. I lowered his head softly onto the tile, watching his eyes slowly close.

I peered at the films. Dr. Silvan traced his esophagus on the x-ray, showing me that it looked abnormal and stretched out. She surmised the condition was probably congenital.

"I'm recommending a daily dose of acid controller, adding more fiber-rich foods to his diet, and slowing down the pace at which he consumes his meals."

I was capable of administering a daily pill and changing up his diet, but stopping him from gulping down his food in thirty seconds or less? That would require some thought.

"Thank you," I said.

"You're welcome." She paused for a minute and then said, "One more thing. I think you should consider putting him on Prozac to calm him down. That would control his hyperactivity."

"Prozac? Do you think that's the right thing to do?" I looked at Magic still sprawled out on the floor. "Are there side effects?" My face flushed as I spat out the questions about the medication.

"It can cause stomach issues in some dogs, but I think in Magic's case, because of his overexcitability, the positives of the drug overshadow the risks."

Stomach issues? I didn't want more stomach issues. Her suggestion to administer a potentially gut-compromising drug to manage his anxiety seemed counterintuitive to everything we discussed. If I wasn't worried about his temperament, why was she continuing to pursue the topic? She didn't live with the dog.

"You could always consult a dog behaviorist," she continued matter-of-factly. "They're professionals who analyze animal behavior and can help owners understand why their animals act the way they do."

I nodded. "Yes, I'm aware of that. Thanks for the info." With that comment, the conversation was over. I turned my back to her as she walked out the door, resuming my position on the floor with Magic.

Twenty minutes later, he slowly lifted his head off my lap and looked at me with glassy eyes. I bent down and kissed the top of his head. "How's my sweet boy? I know you're tired, but let's get out of here."

"Don't like this place."

I paid the bill and made a mental note never to return to that clinic. After my conversation with Dr. Silvan, I administered the acid controller tab once a day.

Although his digestive condition slightly improved, I learned that the long-term use of acid controllers was controversial because they could cause kidney disease and vomiting. I wondered why the veterinarian hadn't cautioned me about the acid controller's side effects. Maybe because she was so focused on giving me a lecture about Magic's excitable personality, she forgot to mention that little tidbit. The fact that she labeled Magic as a hyperactive dog after one visit to her office seemed presumptive. Thinking back to our conversation made the hair on the back of my neck bristle. But as my anger flared, for Magic's sake, I had to set aside my frustrations with Dr. Silvan and direct my attention to figuring out how to help him feel better.

I took the vet's advice into consideration and researched other treatments, too. I made an appointment for Magic to be examined by a highly skilled veterinarian in Flagstaff who diagnosed him with irritable bowel syndrome. She recommended I change his food to a hydrolyzed plant formula. Within three weeks of his new diet, the digestive issues disappeared, and I discontinued the acid controller. I bought a food maze bowl with a raised pattern designed to slow down his food intake. His new daily exercise program expanded to Frisbee in the morning, a walk in the afternoon, and an evening run around the park to manage his frenzied bouts of energy.

I wasn't naïve enough to think that this plan would solve all our issues, but it ruled out the use of medication. I felt empowered that I had been a voice for Magic. I challenged Dr. Silvan's diagnosis that Magic had psychiatric disorders that could only be resolved with anti-depressants. The encounter with Dr. Silvan led me to realize that making decisions for Magic wasn't all that different from the parental decisions I made for our children. As a parent, I did the best I could to raise Charlie, Seth, Maddie, and Magic using available resources, but it was mother's intuition that helped me make the right choices.

23

KINDRED SPIRITS

I thought Magic would forget about his sensational Houdini dog escapes after he lived with us for a while, but sadly his fear of physical barriers and separation continued. It was impossible for me to go anywhere around the house without him watching my every move.

The patio door was his nemesis. Even his daring athleticism was no match for a glass barrier. If I wandered toward the patio door, he'd be ready to spring into action. As soon as I reached for the handle, I'd feel the weight of his chest on the back of my legs. Like Velcro, he'd be on my heels as I stepped outside, weaving his way between my legs just in case I abruptly changed my mind and stepped back inside. He rarely felt comfortable enough to stay outside by himself unless I left the door cracked far enough for him to slip inside on a moment's notice. I endured geckos and blasts of warm air to encourage him to enjoy the fresh air and sunshine.

In September, the weather was still too hot to exercise the pooches anywhere but in the pool. The temperature of the water made it feel more like a bath, reaching ninety degrees. I headed to the pool with a handful of new tennis balls I'd brought from the garage, and both Maddie and Magic stood ready for the first lob.

"Throw it, throw it, throw it."

Magic barked in defiance if I didn't pick up the balls fast enough. After an hour and three chewed-up tennis balls, Magic's belly had swelled to twice its normal size. I announced the game was over and stuffed the soggy toys in the trash can, signaling the end of the activity. Maddie and Magic sprawled out on the deck to dry in the sun.

Magic rolled over on his back. *"Navy Seal workout completed."*

His legs twitched and then slowly relaxed, flopping open, exposing his bulging belly. With his neck tilted to the side, his ear perfectly cushioned his head. The sun's glare forced his eyes closed. Looking at Magic's tranquil body basking in the sun, I figured while he enjoyed a nap, I would take a shower. As I slipped through the small opening of the patio door, I peered back at Magic. He looked like a tired and happy dog.

Quietly, I entered the master bedroom, closing the door behind me. The house had become stuffy from the months of air conditioning, making the idea of a little fresh air, warm or not, appealing to me. I opened the tall, narrow window next to the shower. It had a mesh screen held delicately in place by eight pins spaced evenly along the frame.

The steam shower was gigantic and had a floor-to-ceiling glass door engineered to keep in the condensation. Because of the massive size of the glass, it yielded a view of the sinks and cabinets as well as a portion of our bedroom. I stripped down, opened the shower door, turned on the water, and twirled around, enjoying the rush of water until something caught my eye.

Startled by the crashing noise, I let out a scream as a blur of black fur with bulging eyes, splaying legs, and flaring nostrils zoomed by, riding on some sort of board contraption that resembled a sleigh.

Magic must have backed up to the fence and charged at the open window. With all four paws he made contact with the screen, snapping it off the pins. Riding the wire-mesh frame, he crashed into the bath area like a launched torpedo. Our sleigh rider toppled potted plants before plowing into a pile of clothes, grounding him to a dead stop.

I was in shock, unable to comprehend what had just happened. Wet and soapy, I opened the door and stepped out of the shower. There, in full view, was a dog that needed to be checked for injuries, a contorted screen that had to be replaced, and a window jamb that required repair.

Magic bounded over the edge of the crumpled screen and ran toward me with ears pricked forward and a raised tail.

"Found you."

"Magic, are you okay? Did you hurt yourself? I can't believe you just flew through the window."

"Flying-is-fun."

I tried to hold back a smile as he jumped on me. His eyelashes, dusted with potting soil, lofted dirt into the air as he blinked. The muck on his flank spanned his body to the tip of his tail, and after one wag, soil soared through the air and peppered my legs, sticking in patches and giving me the appearance of a speckled Easter egg.

"Magic, you're crazy," I said, running my hands over his back, legs and tummy. "Let me see those paws." I sighed, "At least you didn't get hurt. Good thing we don't have to go to the vet today."

Magic's ears folded into the side of his head. *"Yes, good thing."*

"But I'll be cleaning up for hours."

"Sorry. Had to find you."

I washed the potting soil off in the shower, toweled dry, and dressed in an old pair of shorts and t-shirt. Armed with a steady stream of cleaning supplies and a brush to free Magic's coat of lingering potting soil, I prepared to tackle the wreckage.

As I scrubbed the floor, picked up the clay pot pieces, and inspected the window frame, I realized Magic was willing to risk hurting himself by jumping through a screened window in order to be with me. I could relate to how Magic was feeling because during my childhood, the feeling of being left behind, separated from the people I loved, left me unable to cope, too.

Case in point.

I remember one time my parents were leaving for a trip that didn't include me. I unpacked their suitcases, tossing their clothes on the floor to dissuade them from leaving. My parents enjoyed their busy social life. They loved attending various parties and events their friends hosted on most weekends.

By the age of six, I knew the routine every Friday and Saturday night, weekend after weekend, year after year. My father, dressed in his coat and tie, would wander into the living room and sit down at the piano. He'd open a music book and select a tune from one of Mom's favorite Broadway shows. That would be my cue to run back to the bedroom to watch my mother add the final touches to her outfit: pearls, a scarf, a special purse.

When she made her grand entrance into the living room, the music stopped abruptly. Their departure was imminent and there was nothing I could do.

Dad would spin around on the piano bench.

"Honey, you look beautiful tonight."

"Thank you. Do you think the scarf is too much?"

"No, you look perfect."

Dad would help Mom with her coat, give me a hug, and they would walk out the front door. I hated that moment, feeling empty as I peered through the side windows, watching him escort my mother to the car and then drive off, headlights fading. Dragging my feet, I let the babysitter lead me into the kitchen for the meal my mother had left us. It's not that I was abandoned in the sense that my parents didn't love or care for me, but somehow, in my distorted thinking, I felt orphaned. The company of sitters never measured up to the two people I most wanted around me. I worried when they went out that they wouldn't return. I willed myself to stay up until they arrived home, drifting in and out of nightmares of them in a fatal car accident. I wrapped myself in my mother's chenille bathrobe, breathing in the scent of her perfume. By the age of ten, the debilitating feeling of being left behind went away as I formed friendships with my peers. But in remembering my childhood struggles, I wondered if Magic's reaction to being left alone at the house was any different than when my parents left me on Saturday nights. I tried to imagine how Magic must have felt the day his family abandoned him on the streets. At least my parents didn't desert me, even though it felt like that at times. Could I blame him for keeping me in his sight and experiencing a meltdown every time I left? If the emotional pang of being separated from loved ones had affected me, how could I expect Magic's reaction to be any different?

THE WORST DOG EVER

W hen our family went out of town, we had to find care for Maddie and Magic. I mistakenly thought we had a number of options for their safe keeping until one by one they were eliminated from the list. We had hoped to rely on friends or family to watch them, but nobody expressed an interest in pet sitting after Magic joined the pack. I considered scheduling a dog walker to come to the house twice a day to feed and exercise them, but I worried Magic couldn't cope with the long hours of isolation. There were a number of boarding facilities in the area, but the idea of housing him in a kennel scared me. I feared he would suffer an injury attempting another daring Houdini dog escape. There was only one other choice: hire a dog sitter to stay with them at our house.

I was fortunate to locate two dependable candidates who expressed an interest in the job. Katrina, a veterinary tech, who was referred by a friend, and Marianne, the receptionist at my prior workplace. At first, I worried that the four-page manual entitled "Survival Instructions," ——complete with details from their eating and pooping rituals to who to call for various emergencies——might have been a deterrent, but the women both boldly agreed to take on the task. The dogs adored Katrina and Marianne, so Michael and I could relax on vacations knowing our canines were well cared for. We thought we had found the perfect solution to our problem until one summer when neither sitter was available to cover our travel dates. If we didn't want to be stuck at home, we needed to figure out a back-up plan for our pet sitters. But what were our options if Magic couldn't be kenneled?

Several days later, while driving around town, I saw a sign advertising a twenty-four-hour open boarding facility. The concept sounded intriguing, so I pulled the car over and dialed the number.

"Hello, Dog-A-Go-Go Camp, this is Sally. How can I help you?"

"Hi, Sally. This is Lauren. I'm interested in your boarding facility for our two Labrador Retrievers. Would you please give me some information on your program?"

"Sure," she quickly replied. "We're a full service, long or short-term care center for canines only. We offer daily daycare and overnight stays for our guests. The dogs are cage-free day and night and enjoy the freedom to interact with their furry friends while being supervised by one of our staff members. Our facility has several air-conditioned indoor playrooms, an outdoor play yard with a small wading pool, and a designated sleeping area."

"Do you put all the dogs together?" I asked uneasily.

"No, we group them by size."

"How many are in a group?"

"It depends. There are a number of factors to consider, such as age, breed, and temperament. We try to find the best fit for each dog. That's why an evaluation is so important."

"An evaluation?" My stomach lurched.

"Yes. If you're interested in the program, you'll need you to make an appointment to bring your dogs to the facility. We'll keep them for about an hour and a half to see how they interact with our other dogs and staff——you know, to get to know their personalities. While we're conducting the evaluation, you can fill out our application and take a tour of the facility."

"Your concept of cage-free boarding is really important for Magic, our special needs dog." I hesitated, rolling my eyes. *Lauren, really? Why did I say special needs?* "He's a rescue and unfortunately he has issues being in a kennel."

"Oh, no problem. Our environment is less stressful for our guests because they aren't cooped up in a cage. They're able to play and socialize with the other boarders as much or as little as they like. It's a great program for dogs of all ages and activity levels. Our clients love the fact that their dogs are tired when they come to pick them up."

"I think Maddie and Magic would love staying at Dog-a-Go-Go. I just need to know how much you charge for an overnight."

"For two dogs, eight-five dollars."

"Okay, great. Um, one more question. Do I need to stay until the evaluation is over?"

"No, you're free to run errands or go home. We'll call you. When you pick them up, we'll let you know if they have been accepted into the program." There was a silent pause. "Lauren, is there anything else we should know about your dogs? I'm assuming they don't have aggression issues."

"No. They haven't bitten another dog... or person, for that matter." My heartbeat quickened thinking about Sally's question. *Should I warn her that Magic has high play drive and boundless energy? Nope, not a good idea. That information won't be helpful in Magic's evaluation process. Besides, these people are experienced handlers. Surely, they've had to deal with some other energetic dogs. Lauren, stop worrying.*

"Lauren? Lauren, are you there?"

"Yes, sorry. I was just thinking that I need to clean the bathroom floor."

"Are you interested in visiting our facility today?"

"Yes, what time do you have available?"

"Does one-o'clock work?"

"Yes, thanks. See you at one."

I hung up the phone. "Yeah!" I said, shifting the car into drive. But by the time I pulled into our driveway, the hopeful feeling that I had found an alternative to a sitter was clouded by the fear of what might happen during Magic's evaluation.

At twelve-forty, I harnessed both dogs. Magic trotted to the front door first.

"Ready."

"Listen, Magic. You need to be on good behavior today. No craziness."

"Me, crazy?"

"Magic, stop barking."

"Are we going to the park?"

"Enough already," I said, snapping on his leash. Magic followed on my heels until we reached the car. "Magic, sit."

"Can't. Too excited."

"Can you wait just one second?" I asked while opening the door. Magic leaped past me onto the seat.

"Apparently the answer to that question is no," I said, reaching over and strapping him in. "Wahoo, Magic, we're off to camp!"

"Camp? Hey, what happened to the park?"

"Can you please take a chill pill while I get Maddie?"

"Maybe you need one."

The ten-minute car ride seemed like forever with the constant stream of barking in the vehicle. Pulling into a parking spot, I prepared for battle, stuffing my purse under the seat and dropping the keys into my back pocket. With both hands freed up, I was ready for any wrestling match that was about to unfold. I opened the door, shortened Magic's leash, and released his seat belt. As soon as he heard the click, he rocketed out of the car, pulling me into the bushes right next to the front door.

"No. Magic, not there." But it was too late. When Sally opened the door to greet me, his puddle of urine oozed across the walkway.

"Hi," I said. "Sorry about that. If you have a bucket of water, I'd be happy to wash off your entrance." I was already apologizing and I hadn't even made it inside the building.

"Don't worry about it," she said. "You must be Lauren. Don't you have another dog?"

"Yes. She's still in the car."

"Why don't I hold Magic's leash while you get her?"

"Thanks. That would be great." Maddie made a graceful exit from the car and walked up to the entrance of the building. Sally motioned us to follow her to the admin desk located just through the door. The sound of jingling chains and tags danced in the background. Looking behind the desk, I saw the layout included several large rooms with a walkway down the middle. Each room had a surrounding four-foot wall.

Maddie and Magic's ears pricked forward as they listened to all the activity. I knew Magic's mounting curiosity meant only one thing: a bark fest was about to explode. But as Magic threw his head into the air, a burly staff member with a beard and a nametag that read "John" walked up to us.

"Hi. You must be Maddie and Magic's owner."

"Yes. I'm Lauren. Nice to meet you, John."

He reached out his palm and held it for the dogs to smell. "I'm here to take them to one of our play areas. I'll see you in a bit."

"Okay. Thanks." I handed him the leashes and watched the black and white tail-waggers follow him down the hallway.

Sally called me over to her desk. "Here's our application. When you're finished, I'll take you on a tour of the facility."

I tried to concentrate on filling out the questionnaire, but I couldn't stop worrying about whether Magic would pass his test. As I nervously tapped my pen, sweat that had beaded up on my fingertips dropped onto the form.

"All done," I said, handing her the damp pages. "Here are their vaccine records."

"Great. Let me show you around." As we walked down the long hallway, the sound of rowdy canines grew louder. To the right, there was a large room with concrete floors and a multitude of dog beds in every color lined up along the walls. There were plush blankets and pillows scattered in the middle.

"This is our designated quiet area for dogs looking to take a break from the action, and also where they sleep at night." Sally walked across the four-foot hallway. She stopped to rest her elbows on the ledge of the wall and said, "On this side of the facility, we split the room in half to make two play spaces. This one is for small dogs. We've got our regulars here today."

She pointed as she listed their names. "There's Augie, Taco, Jelly-bean, Cookie, Toto, and Trixie. The next playroom is for large breeds——that's where your dogs will be hanging out." Sally again gestured for me to follow her.

As the front room came into view, I saw a caramel-colored Labradoodle engaged in a game of tug of war with a chisel-chested boxer. They were snarling, throwing their heads from side to side, and clamping down on the fraying rope that was slowly thinning out to one long strand. A brown and white short-haired mutt and an Australian Shepherd were supervising the game. Mary, a woman with a ponytail dressed in jeans and a t-shirt, stood in the middle of the action, playing referee.

Sally was busy explaining the daily routine and feeding procedures when John opened the door to the playroom.

"Mary," John called. "We've got a new one. His name is Magic. Can you supervise while I get his sister? I'll be back in a minute."

Over a wave of yelps, Mary cheerfully approved the plan.

Magic darted through the doorway, passed by Mary, and madly searched the area for an available toy. He found a red rubber ball, picked it up mid-stride, and began running laps along the wall. The other dogs were soon following him, yelping with excitement. When John returned with Maddie and let her off her leash, she immediately joined the frenzied circle of dogs chasing Magic. As the booms of barking escalated to a feverish pitch, John's face fell. His mouth opened when the whirling dervish leading the pack abruptly stopped at his feet and spit out the slimy toy.

"Throw it. Hurry." Magic leaped into the air, woofing with such force his feet barely touched the floor.

The group of panting dogs swirled around their new playmate like he was a celebrity. But Magic couldn't be bothered with his adoring fans. He jumped on the ball, pushing it closer to John.

"Need you to throw it now."

John wiped beads of sweat off his brow. He shot a look of exasperation to Sally and then at me. Magic was not delivering a stellar performance. In the span of ten minutes, he had turned the whole place upside down. Sally asked me to go with her to the entrance. When we stopped at her desk, she looked at me with raised eyebrows and tight lips. "Magic is pretty energetic, isn't he?"

"Yes, he loves chasing a ball. Actually, he loves playing with all kinds of toys."

"I can see that." She paused before continuing. "Well, alright. I'll see you back here in an hour and a half."

"Please call me on my cell."

"Will do."

Only thirty minutes had lapsed when I received a breathless call from John. "Lauren, would you please come and pick up your dogs?"

"Yes, of course. Is everything okay?" I asked.

"Everything's fine."

I hurried back to the facility to collect Maddie and Magic. Sally met me at the door with a strained look on her face. "Maddie is a wonderful dog. We'd be happy to take her, but I'm afraid we can't accept Magic. He requires more supervision and attention than we can give to any one dog."

"Oh. Well, thank you for giving him a try. Where is he?"

"Both of them are with John in the play area. I'll take you there." Sally and I walked in silence down the long hallway until we reached the area. I peered over the wall at the play area. I saw John trying to corral Magic away from the pack. He looked exhausted; his face was tense, and his shoulders were slumped forward.

"Hi, John. I'll take my dogs off your hands, now."

"Thanks," he said heaving a sigh of relief. "If you continue down the hall, you'll see a door on the left. Meet me there. I'll grab Magic first and then go back and get Maddie."

I glanced over at Sally. "I'm going to get the dogs. Be back in a minute." I had only taken a few steps before wild yips and a chorus of barking rang in my ears. I turned around to see a stocky, middle-aged woman with her hair twisted into a bun, jogging toward Sally with her coiffed French poodle.

"Sally! Oh Sally, thank goodness. I'm late again," she announced, forcing the leash into Sally's hand. "You can check Fluffy in, right? I have to run. Thanks!"

Magic, hearing Fluffy's joyful yips, broke away from John's grip and ran along the edge of the playroom wall listening intently to the barking coming from the other side of the partition.

"What's going on? Party? Dog fest? Here I come."

Magic backed up five feet, launched himself, and soared over the playroom wall like a gazelle, landing squarely on top of the poodle. Fluffy's owner screamed. I scrambled to the scene, yanking Magic by the collar, rolling him off the dog's back.

"Magic! What are you doing?" I yelled.

"Sorry. Just wanted to say hello."

"Get-your-dog-away-from-us!" the woman bellowed, pointing her index finger at me. "You're going to pay the vet bills for the injuries your dog has done to Fluffy."

Sally blushed. "I'm sorry, Mrs. Finkelworth, this has never happened before."

Amidst all the confusion, the poodle popped back up on all fours and shook out her coat. She took a few steps and sniffed Magic's face before bowing down on her front paws, ready to play.

"Oh my gosh, I'm so sorry. Magic didn't mean to jump on your dog. It was an accident. I'll give you my name and num…"

"Your dog is a menace!" Mrs. Finkelworth shouted at me, jerking the playful poodle away from Magic. Sneering at Sally, she brayed, "I don't want my dog participating in a program that allows this kind of disorderly conduct. Fluffy and I are leaving."

"Please, wait a minute," Sally pleaded. "I'm sure we can work this out."

"I'm not interested in working anything out with you," she retorted as she turned her back on us.

I watched her march down the center corridor, Fluffy heeling at her side. Feeling humiliated, I dodged eye contact with Sally and looked at John, still red-faced, standing in the play area. "I'm sorry this happened. If you bring Maddie to the door, I'll grab her and leave.

Thank you for giving the dogs the opportunity to try out your facility."

Mustering the courage to look at Sally, I said, "Magic's not a bad dog." I shook my head. "Really, he's not. He just gets a little too exuberant sometimes." Sally gave me a blank stare. There was no way Magic would ever be able to redeem his reputation. He hadn't just been asked to leave. He had been expelled.

John walked over to me with Maddie. "Thanks," I said. Tightening up the leads, I walked out of the building as fast as possible to distance myself from the experience. I added Sally and John to the long list of people who openly characterized Magic as an incorrigible dog.

The expulsion from dog camp was so traumatic that I couldn't bear to tell anyone what had happened. I reasoned that if nobody knew about the incident, I could spare myself the embarrassment and protect Magic's reputation. The solution was simple, or so I thought. I kept Magic's mishaps a secret. I downplayed his debacles and fabricated stories to cover up what really happened, like the time Magic pulled me down a mountain chasing a coyote. I suffered a grade two high ankle sprain and numerous cactus spines jammed into my back. When people asked me about the cast on my leg, my answer was that I rolled my foot over a curb. Thankfully, I didn't have to explain why there were pieces of cactus lodged under my skin.

But I couldn't always protect him from other people's disdain. Once, he escaped out our front door, sprinted to a neighbor's house, and ran through their screen door in pursuit of dog toys and kibble. The bent frame and torn mesh cost me two-hundred dollars. The cost of restoring an amicable relationship with my neighbor required another type of payment——food gifts. I baked cinnamon bread and dozens of chocolate chip cookies to smooth things over.

Magic's behavior was also problematic when we walked in the forest behind our cabin. He couldn't resist the opportunity to interact with every person and pooch on the trail, often giving the appearance of being possessed.

Magic's bark was a constant source of frustration for anyone who had to listen to him sound off. The decibel level of a loud rock concert is one-hundred twenty. Magic's bark must have registered at least ninety, which would explain why the boom often shook the windows in our house. But the volume at which he chose to communicate wasn't the only way he scared people. He demonstrated his hyper personality and exuberance by jumping high in the air, narrowly missing people on the way down. He didn't growl or display aggression, but because of his demonstrative greeting behavior his actions were frequently misunderstood. One morning while off leash in the woods, he spied an older woman and her springer spaniel. He bolted ahead and ran circles around them, barking so loudly he couldn't hear me shouting to come back. Magic danced around the spaniel trying to engage him in a game of play while the woman stood paralyzed in fear. When the spaniel shied away and sat by its owner's side, Magic tried a different approach. He darted from side to side, barely avoiding a collision with the dog and woman. The woman, afraid that Magic was going to land on her, took a step backward, tripped and fell. I rushed over to Magic, snapped on his leash and helped her up. Although she didn't sustain any physical injuries, she was so traumatized she stopped walking in the woods. I wrote her a letter of apology and left flowers on her doorstep for a week.

The question of why I kept a problematic dog persisted because my fictitious stories didn't cover up Magic's zest for living. There was only one way to stop the cross-examinations. I had to be impervious to the derogatory comments from other people about Magic's behavior by not taking them personally. Maybe I wasn't always proud of what he did, but I loved him. I felt the same about my kids when they messed up. I didn't desert them when they needed me to be there for them. Just like my children, Magic was part of my family. *Lauren, be strong. Make a commitment to cope with the backlash of Magic's behavior in the same way I do for the kids. Don't use the convenient excuse that he's a dog to minimize this situation.* Through perseverance, I decided to outwardly shrug off negative remarks and inwardly soothe my bruised ego.

Magic gave me several opportunities to practice resilience. Whether he was being kicked out of dog camp or running through my neighbor's screen door, he taught me how to take a stand for him, and as a result, for myself.

When we got home from Dog-A-Go-Go Camp, I sat on the floor beside Magic, picked up his head, and kissed his nose. "Just so you know, I don't care what people say. I'm not giving up on you even though people think I should." I had finally realized that only one person's opinion of Magic mattered: mine.

25

FOOD SOOTHES THE SOUL

I would gladly have matched Magic against any truffle hog in a fungus sniffing contest. Truffles are only valuable when harvested at their peak aroma, and with Magic's exceptional smeller and tireless pursuit of anything edible, he would have been able to run circles around a four-hundred-pound pig.

Labs tend not to have an on/off switch when it comes to food consumption. Their propensity to overeat, a phenomenon believed to be wired into the brain at birth, presents a lifelong challenge for an owner. Magic was no exception to that rule, but his glutinous tendencies and obsession with food-seeking behavior seemed to be motivated by more than just hunger.

Searching for food was a game he loved to play. His clever approach led me to believe he enjoyed figuring out a winning strategy. His technical skills were impressive. Whatever games I came up with, he quickly learned how to play them and, like a goal-scoring machine in a soccer game, he rarely missed an opportunity to take a shot. Most times, the soccer ball landed in the back of the net, positively reinforcing his winning streak. But was there another reason he fixated on food hunting games? I suspected his compulsive nature played a role.

Magic didn't have a discriminating palate. He consumed anything he could get his paws on. Serving size did not matter, either. For example, when he lifted a one-cup container of dry peanut butter protein powder off the counter, pried off the plastic top, and consumed the entire contents, I'm sure he wasn't concerned that he had eaten one hundred and fifty grams of protein in one treat. He believed a large, warehouse-size bag of chips was to be enjoyed in one sitting and showed no restraint when he chowed down on three sleeves of cookies that had the equivalent of two thousand three hundred and eight-five calories. I never thought he'd carefully screw off the plastic lid of the sample jar of sugar scrub I was formulating for Christmas gifts and lick the container clean. Based on Magic's approval, I surmised my recipe of lime zest, lime juice, sugar, and olive oil would be sought-after by everyone, whether enjoyed as an exfoliant or an afternoon snack. By age two he had tried more types of food than our teenage children, and unlike some adults, he loved the taste of mushrooms, spinach, and Brussels sprouts. Because of his propensity to consume anything remotely edible, I thought he might be part goat. He didn't give up easily, relying on goat resourcefulness.

The lightning speed at which he gulped down entire pizzas and loaves of bread baffled us. We rarely caught him in the act of pulling food off the counter, jumping up on a chair to clean off a dinner plate, or wedging his nose into the slightly ajar pantry door for his personal smorgasbord. Other than licking his lips and looking a bit rounder in the tummy, there were no telltale signs the thief had struck, apart from the issues he had at the other end——but that's one topic I don't want to talk about.

Above all else, I knew Magic's favorite food was butter. He could smell the sweet cream from twenty feet away, and when left on the counter unattended, the whole stick would disappear in one gulp, including the paper wrapper. Although butter was at the top of his list, any high-fat food came in as a close second. I stored grapeseed, avocado, and coconut oil on the third shelf of the pantry, out of reach. But the large gallon jug of olive oil, too tall for the rack, had to be stowed on the floor. I briefly worried that the jug would be accessible to Magic but decided if I was vigilant about closing the laundry door and pantry closet, there wouldn't be a problem. *Lauren, who are you kidding? Being vigilant about keeping that pantry closet closed? I don't think so. I access that panty maybe fifteen times a day. I often leave it open. Wasn't that the reason I had to cancel my hair appointment at the last minute? I had to turn around halfway to the salon because I couldn't remember whether the pantry door was left open. How many times can I use the excuse that I lost track of time and rushed out of the house?*

Closing doors everywhere in the house seemed to be the single most effective way to keep Magic out of trouble. I tried to build five minutes into my schedule to inspect the house before my departure, giving each door a nudge to make sure it was fully secured.

That strategy worked perfectly until the night I was running late for a New Year's Eve dinner dance. Poor planning resulted in scrambling to get out of the house on time.

"Michael, we have to hustle. I hate being rushed!" I yelled.

"Did you feed the dogs and let them out?"

"They're all set. Let's go. We're going to be late."

Magic trotted into the bedroom and jumped onto the end of the bed.

"Look, Magic knows we're leaving him tonight. He's already sulking," I said uneasily.

"Not happy."

I turned to look at Magic. "You need to be a good boy while Mom and Dad are out tonight."

"Treats would help." Magic watched as we put on our coats.

"See you later, Magic," Michael said. "Everything secure in the house?"

"Yes, yes, let's go."

"Where's my treat?"

As I slammed the door to the garage, I said, "Dinner, dancing, live music. Oh honey, we will always remember this New Year's Eve party." That night we danced and celebrated the start of the new year with our best friends. After one last toast, a round of hugs, and the promise of enduring relationships with our friends, we climbed in the car and made the short drive home. I looked at my watch as we pulled into the driveway—— two am. When was the last time we were out that late? I couldn't remember. As the garage door opened, the familiar sound of Magic's bark was noticeably absent. That was not a good sign. Like a match igniting a piece of paper, my face flushed.

While Michael parked in the garage, I jogged to the door, my throat feeling as dry as the desert. Pushing the door open, I stepped from the garage into the laundry room, switched on the light, and stared at the sea of oil shimmering on the tile floor. The neck of a green bottle, tipped on its side, jutted out from the open pantry door. A chewed-up cap lay mangled under the drips of oil still oozing from the bottle. I sidestepped the puddle and picked up the jug. It was half empty. The white travertine flooring had a five-foot greenish stain where the substance had penetrated the porous stone.

"Oh my gosh!" I shrieked. "I can't believe it. I left the pantry door open."

Michael came barreling through the door. "What? What? Aaaah!" He skidded and tumbled into the middle of the pool of oil.

"Yuck," he said, watching droplets of grease roll off his fingers. "You have to be kidding me. Magic!"

But Magic was nowhere to be found. Michael grabbed a towel from the top of the dryer, took off his shoes, wiped off the bottoms, and then followed the greasy paw prints leading to the family room. He took two steps onto the soggy carpet before seeing his socks engulfed in a pile of vomit. "Ahhhhh, I'm so mad at that dog."

"What now?" I yelled, from the laundry room.

"There's vomit on the carpet and I stepped in it." Michael took off his socks and trudged barefoot into the dining room. Magic cowered under the dining room table. His glistening, oil-soaked ears were pasted to the side of his head. He inched further away from Michael.

Told you I wanted a treat.

Michael crouched down to make eye contact. "Magic, come," he grumbled.

Don't want to come. Magic moved backwards; his muzzle skimming the carpet.

"Forget it. I'll deal with you later." Michael walked into the kitchen looking for a paper towel to clean off his socks.

"Hon, I'm out in the laundry room mopping up oil. Is he going to need a bath tonight?"

"I'm in the kitchen cleaning puke off my socks."

"Oh, sorry," I said, joining him in the kitchen. "We can bathe him tomorrow. Maybe you can towel off the oil for now. I'm going to walk around the rest of the house to assess the damage."

Michael held up the puke-covered socks, looking like he might throw them at me.

"Sorry. I'll clean up Magic."

After changing clothes, we grabbed rags, carpet cleaner, and a bucket. There were paw prints on the tile in the hallway and wide smudges of oil on the area rugs where Magic had rolled his muzzle to remove the greasy residue. We decided to start in the family room and clean up the bile on the carpet because we had no clue what to do with the tile.

"I feel terrible. This is my fault. I was in a hurry. I didn't check all the doors before we left." I gave a big sigh. "This has taken all the fun out of our evening and the house is a wreck. I know I've asked this question before, but why do you think he does stuff like this? I thought Maddie would keep him company while we were gone but it's obvious there was something else going on. He's a little cray-cray. Maybe he does need a doggie therapist."

Michael gave me a blank stare. "I don't know what his problem is, but whatever it is, he makes our life difficult. He has a family who loves and cares for him. What more can we possibly do? I think you're making excuses for his behavior."

"What are you saying? You want me to return him to the rescue? I'm afraid we're way past the return date."

Michael looked angry. "I don't want to talk about this."

"This is the worst New Year's Eve ever," I said, heading to the bedroom. "Shoot! Where's Magic?"

"Last time I saw him he was hiding under the table."

"I'll deal with him," I said, tearing off a paper towel and walking toward the dining room. "Magic, come."

Magic's head slowly peered around the corner. Every step he made was tentative, as if he was walking in quicksand. He stopped two feet away from me, avoiding eye contact and hanging his tail straight to the ground like a pencil.

"Sit, Magic." I knelt on my knees and reached out to gently wipe his glistening muzzle and ears. "Are you okay, buddy? You probably have a bad tummy ache."

He placed his oily paw over my arm and locked eyes with me. *"Sorry about the mess."*

"Magic, it's a good thing I put up with you."

"Yes, good thing."

I pulled the patio door open. "Go pee." He ran past me, disappearing into the night. This whole fiasco could have been avoided if I had been vigilant in securing the house. I felt guilty for misdirecting my anger at Michael. *Lauren, answer the question. How many more times am I going to make the same mistake?* As I stood there thinking, Magic slipped through the open crack of the patio door and slinked into our bedroom.

26

THE ARTIST

Over the span of the next couple months, Magic developed new skills to satiate his imagined hunger when he was alone in the house. He appeared to be calmer when mentally engaged in some sort of activity. One of his favorite exercises was to forage in the house for opportunities to keep himself busy until I got home. His pursuit kept his mind tracked on finding an obscure treat, a newfangled object he deemed a play toy, or a personal item that carried my scent. I was thankful that he didn't chew on drywall or mark furniture, but I feared that leaving Magic to his own devices would spell disaster.

Magic knew that my purse, left unsupervised on the kitchen table, offered an easy relief from his sugar cravings. I'd catch him gently tugging the handles until it fell to the ground, spilling the contents like a broken pinata. When my bag was slung over the side of the chair, he would arch his neck and dive to the bottom for mints, sticks of gum, and flavored lip balms. After catching him looting my purse a second time, I moved his new obsession into the bedroom behind a carefully closed door.

Knowing Magic's propensity to get into trouble, Michael and I made an agreement to always store personal items out of reach and relegate him to the kitchen and family room area where we could keep an eye on him. We learned that lesson from Charlie and Seth when they were toddlers. If Magic silently disappeared, that usually meant he had gotten into something. Our vow to follow through on our plan was working. We had twenty-three straight days of no mishaps. With the exchange of a high five, we celebrated with new-found confidence that our Magic problems were over.

The next evening at seven o'clock, we made the snap decision to see a seven-thirty movie.

"We need to hustle if we want to see the opening credits. I'll let the dogs out. You grab the keys. I'll meet you in the garage," Michael said.

Because Michael drove like Mario Andretti, we got to our seats as the previews started. The film was fabulous and funny, the perfect antidote to our stressful week. We talked about the plot on the ride home and were still chatting about the dynamic ending as we pulled up to the garage.

"Magic's not barking. That's not good. Wait, did I … Noooo, I didn't bring my purse tonight. Darn! I think I left it on the dresser and..."

"Let me guess," Michael interrupted. "You didn't close the door."

"I didn't because I thought you'd close it after you grabbed your wallet."

Bursting through the garage door, I yelled, "Magic! Where are you?" I looked around the kitchen hoping Magic would appear at any moment. Then something colorful caught my eye. Shiny smears of a foreign substance speckled the tile. Was it crayons? Orange-colored body lotion? Lipstick? I reached down and brushed my fingertips across the surface. It was soft and waxy. With no greeting from Magic, I followed the mean-dering trail of smudged tiles that led to the end of the hallway. I found Magic lying down, eyes glassed over. He picked up his head but quickly looked away from my gaze as he started to pant. His chest muscles tight-ened, and ears rotated backwards, almost disappearing from sight. A flashback of what happened on New Year's Eve unraveled any strand of sympathy I had for him. Hands on my hips, I started yelling.

"Oh my gosh! Why do you get into everything? We can't we leave you alone for one minute!" I glared at him. "Is this lipstick? Is this lipstick? What a mess. Look at your toenails. And your tail. Really? You sat on my favorite shade? This came from my purse, didn't it? Didn't it?"

Magic's pinned ears were flat against his head. *"Sorry."*

I stomped off, leaving Magic in the hallway, and headed for the bedroom in search of my bag. As I peeked around the master bedroom door, nothing could have prepared me for what I was about to see scattered all over the area rug. A dented tin of spearmint mints lay on its side. Partially shredded gum wrappers dotted the area. The zebra-striped cosmetic bag was empty, and every lipstick was ravaged. Three plastic tubes of liquid lip gloss were bitten in half and the chocolate and peppermint flavors were sucked dry. The six metal-cased tubes had embedded teeth marks where he had pried them open. Large chunks of lipstick, broken into various pieces, lay discarded alongside the bureau.

It didn't take long to figure out the pink, purple, red, and coral lipstick pigments had become Magic's art medium. I suspected our emerging artist used the beige rug as his canvas, creating a unique abstract masterpiece. He must have applied the colorful swirls in the center of the rug as he tried to wipe the lipstick off his nose and muzzle. The bold patterns of red and pink marks that arched across the top of the rug must have been made by raking toenails. I imagined the splotches of purple that faded out to the sides might have been made from his tail swishing back and forth. It was a beautiful rendition of an Arizona sunset. He authenticated it with his signature, a smeared pink paw print in the bottom corner. I had always longed to buy an original piece of artwork but flinched at the sky-high cost. Until I personally experienced the scope of the work from our emerging artist, "Magic Van Gogh," I couldn't comprehend the sheer effort of producing such a masterpiece.

"You've got to be kidding me," I said, walking around the perimeter of the rug. "Michael? Michael, where are you? You've got to see this. Michael!"

Michael walked into the bedroom holding up his glass. "I thought I'd grab a beer before…"

"Look at this. Can you believe what this dog gets into? Why did we put down white travertine tile? Oh yeah, that was before we adopted Magic."

Michael silently panned the floor a moment longer. "This is ridiculous. We leave him for a couple hours and this is what happens? Look at this mess——just because we left a door open. I don't even know where to start with the clean-up."

"He's beyond frustrating. You think you're mad? I have to replace all my favorite lipsticks." I retrieved a box of makeup remover pads from under the bathroom sink. "Here's some for you. Try it out on the travertine."

"I think you'd better hire a cleaning specialist. Add another two hundred for a new rug." Michael thought for a moment. "Based on our clean-up expenses, it looks like your lipstick replacement budget is going to be cut."

I scowled at him. "Fine. I'm going to put this designer rug up for sale for five thousand dollars. With all that cash we can get the floors cleaned and buy a new rug. That will leave us with a four-thousand-dollar surplus. Guess I'll be able to buy as many lipsticks as I want with that kind of budget."

"Very funny," Michael said flatly.

Magic was where I left him, sprawled out at the end of the hall. When he saw me, he picked up his lipsticked face and quickly turned away. I knelt on my knees, pinning him against the wall. I held his head with my left hand, leaned in with the cleansing tissue, and rubbed his nose so hard he jumped.

"Magic, sit." Magic reluctantly sat on his haunches. With flattened ears, he slowly lowered his head and sank back to the floor. When I reached out to clean his muzzle, he whimpered and cowered. As I pulled out another towelette from the package, the softness in his eyes extinguished my fury. Unable to look away, I dropped the tissue. I felt guilty for being so hard on him, remembering that his previous owners had left him on the streets of Phoenix when he was eleven-months old.

I couldn't let go of the conviction that Magic was a troubled dog who would never be trustworthy in an unsupervised environment. But had I been too hasty in making a judgment about his character and decision-making skills without knowing his history? How could I come to a place of understanding and acceptance if I had no idea what happened in his life before we adopted him?

Looking into Magic's soulful eyes, I remembered a traumatic time in my early twenties during a summer internship when fear and weakness left me broken, trying to survive from one day to the next. I never thought the worst part of the experience would be the response from my father when I returned home after being away for three months. He shamed me. The sting of his rejection cut deeply. All I ever wanted from my father was love and acceptance because he meant the world to me.

Magic's ears rotated backwards as he placed his paw over my arm. *"Pet me. That will help both of us."*

I granted Magic his request, letting my thoughts drift as we sat in silence. It was a summer I'd never forget. Being a youth director on a cruise ship for a summer internship was a departure from any lifestyle I had ever encountered and required an immediate adjustment. The ship, comprising twelve decks, was a self-contained floating city that served as my workplace, home, and social life. I had no idea how challenging it would be to assimilate into that new world where I would have to operate independently, manage my insecurities, and function as a responsible adult every minute of the day and night.

On the first day, the reality of my new assignment sunk in when three enormous tugs pulled our ship out of the harbor, setting us on our navigational course to Bermuda. There was no escaping the outlandish adventure I was about to undertake unless I jumped overboard and swam back to shore.

The second day at sea, I took too much Dramamine to combat seasickness. Barely able to keep my eyes focused, I painted faces on the kids that made them look more like zombies than clowns.

The cruise director expected that I could handle the youth program and assist with adult activities without prior training or support from the staff. One night, he asked me to run the theater lights for the passenger's talent show, but when I couldn't figure out how to use the stage instruments panel, the crowd booed.

That's how my summer job began. Riddled with self-doubt, I was unprepared to be thrown into an environment where I would have to cope with feeling alone and overwhelmed with work responsibilities. I fell into bed at night exhausted, but intermittent sleep only yielded temporary relief from my fear of failure. My stomach, tied up in knots, began churning as soon as the alarm clock chimed.

I wanted to build a support network of friends, but the cruise staff, officers, and entertainers were moving from one ship to another every two or three weeks, limiting my opportunity to establish any long-lasting connections. Passengers were on board for one week and any bonding with kids through my activities yielded a tearful good-bye when they disembarked.

From the outside, things looked different than they really were. My life appeared glamorous and sophisticated. Standing on the top deck of the ship, feeling the warm summer winds, I convinced myself I was living the dream. What was I thinking?

Despite the beauty that surrounded me and the surreal lifestyle that any other college student might have envied, I felt restless. Without another person to share the experience, my life seemed superficial. Being only one quarter of the way through the internship, I wondered how I would make it to September. I thought no one else was aware of my struggle until the new cruise director, Allen, asked me to see him in his office.

Allen looked at me with a concerned expression. "I've only been on this ship for three days but I'm worried that you don't seem invested in your job. Is there something personal going on or is something bothering you that I can help with?"

I responded casually, "Thanks for your concern, but no, I'm fine. You can count on me to do the job." The truth was I didn't want him to worry that his youth director would need counseling. I had to figure out how to cope with feeling depressed and alone on my own terms.

The following week, while we were docked in Bermuda, another ship in the fleet moored behind us. As I walked down the gangway, I noticed an attractive, blonde man in a starched, white uniform chatting with my cruise director. I picked up my step, hoping the two would continue their conversation so that I could meet him. "Hi, Allen," I said with a smile.

"Oh, hi, Lauren, I was just talking to Austin, the purser on our sister ship. He tells me they will be sharing our dock all day on Thursdays. Austin, this is Lauren, our youth director."

Was I dreaming or had I just met the sexiest man on the planet? Where had he been hiding all my life?

"Hi," is all I could get out, staring at his marbled blue eyes.

Austin smiled at me. "This is my first time in Bermuda. Would you give me a tour of the isla——?"

"Yes, love to."

"I need to change clothes. Can we meet back here in say, fifteen minutes?"

"That'd be great." I sounded like a high schooler.

After six dates with Austin, I was falling in love. On Thursdays, we rendezvoused at the moped shop, hopped on a tandem motorized bike, and played at the beach all day. With a new person to share my life, everything looked different. I couldn't wait to roll out of bed, and there was a spring in my step that everyone noticed. I slept deeply and felt more invested in my job because I had someone to think about, someone waiting for me every Thursday.

After another glorious day together, we returned the bikes and were heading back to our ships.

"Lauren," Austin said as he grabbed my hand. "I have something to talk to you about. I didn't want to put a damper on our day together, so I waited to tell you that I'm being transferred to another ship on Saturday and won't be coming into Bermuda anymore."

"A damper on my day? This is not happening. They can't transfer you."

"I'm sorry, I don't have a choice. You know how they move people around."

"But I'll never see you again." I felt my voice cracking. "This is not fair."

"I know."

"How am I going to get though the rest of the summer without you?"

"I'll miss you, too, and I'll never forget you. When I think of Bermuda, you'll be the one I remember."

He threw his arms around me, pulled me close, and then sauntered away.

Walking toward the gangway of my ship, I turned and watched as he stepped onto his ship. I waved but he didn't wave back. Had he just dumped me? I hustled up the passageway, walking with my head down, past the officers at the entrance to get to my cabin before sobbing uncontrollably. I fell on the mattress, burying my head in the pillow.

I was heartbroken. The pain of rejection left me feeling abandoned. I felt angry for being so vulnerable. I wanted to believe he loved me, too, but after replaying our last conversation, I realized he was indifferent. The relationship was over.

Staggering into the bathroom to grab some tissues, I stopped cold, catching the image of a red-faced, puffy-eyed girl in the mirror. I looked like I had been in a prize fight. Who was this girl? Not somebody I wanted to be. I needed a new plan. A new me. That meant there would be no staying holed up in my cabin. If I didn't want to go to dinner looking like I had lost a fight, I needed to make a few adjustments. Putting on a new air of confidence, I washed my face, applied new makeup, fluffed up my hair, and headed straight for the dining room.

The food selection was looking especially beautiful. The long winding tables showcased tray after tray of elegant hot and cold appetizers: garden green salads; fruits in all colors of the rainbow; rich soups; cheeses from all over the world; fresh shellfish and fish; meats; and a carving station. There was vegetarian fare: pasta; a medley of sautéed, steamed, and stir-fried vegetables; freshly baked bread; and, of course, decadent desserts. That was just dinner. Later that night there would be a midnight buffet featuring foodie selections from all over the world.

I picked up a plate and helped myself to an assortment of gourmet cheeses, crusty French bread with creamy butter, and a huge bowl of hot spiced lobster bisque. I polished off the cheeses and soup in a matter of minutes. Feeling surprisingly better, I decided to skip the entrees and go straight for dessert.

The glass-enclosed, seven-tiered dessert case displayed individually plated cakes and pastries. I selected the cheesecake that had a purply glaze on top puddled in a sauce dotted with fresh blueberries. I dipped a velvety bite in the sauce, catching a couple plump berries. The cheese lingered on my tongue. Hints of vanilla and slightly sweet blueberries rocked my taste buds. It was delicious. No, it was insanely delicious. Perhaps the best food I had ever eaten. After each forkful I felt a little happier and a lot hungrier. I was starving! I looked longingly at the dessert case. *Maybe just one more*, I'd thought, rationalizing that I only drank two rum swizzles for lunch.

That night in the dining room, surrounded by four empty dessert plates, I discovered a way to heal the parts of me that were broken. With a full tummy I was emotionally fortified to take on anything coming my way. I found my next love and a way to feed my ailing heart: the dessert case. When I looked dejected, the Indonesian crew would feel sorry for me and sneak me into the walk-in freezer where forty-five flavors of ice cream awaited me. Besides the pure enjoyment of savoring the frosty treat, a few scoops before bed kept the nightmares away. But self-soothing by overeating had one serious drawback. A new type of stress surfaced because the extra pounds I had gained made it increasingly difficult to fit into my clothes. Some of the staff started to look at me differently and I could hear whispers of derogative comments about my weight. I felt guilty when I overate, but that didn't stop me from making multiple trips to the dessert case. I had found a way to suppress my feelings of inadequacy by further medicating myself through eating. The daily battle fell into a cycle of self-loathing.

I stopped going to the beach, embarrassed to put on a bathing suit and afraid that someone would judge me for my rounded thighs and bulging belly. I bought a skirt that was two sizes larger and hoped nobody would notice I wore it four times a week. When the photographer took pictures, I hid behind the kids, hoping they would cover up my increasing size. I breathed a sigh of relief when I had only one more week on board. I couldn't wait to get off.

My dad picked me up right where he left me thirteen weeks ago. I was ecstatic to see him. I ran down the gangway and threw my arms around his neck.

"I've missed you and Mom so much."

He looked at me with a puzzled expression. "Is that you under all that?"

I had gained fifteen pounds, which was a lot of weight on my petite frame. I knew I looked heavy, but did he have to make his first statement about my appearance? If that was my father's first comment, how would my mother and friends react?

"So, how was your summer onboard?"

"I learned a lot, but I don't think I would ever want to work full time on a ship again."

"The food must have been good."

The statement stung. I quickly hopped into the car and turned my head toward the window so he wouldn't see me blinking back tears. I wanted to be invisible so I could deflect the judgmental comments that elicited so much shame. How could he say such an unkind thing to me? Like I didn't already know I had to lose weight? Didn't he love me, regardless of how I looked? I was still the same person, whether I gained weight or not, even if I had made bad choices.

Now, sitting on the floor with Magic, I closed my eyes and thought about how unlovable I had felt after that summer on the cruise ship. The pain of that memory still lingered. Magic bumped his head into my thigh. I looked at his partially covered lipstick face. Oh, how I loved seeing that messy face in front of me. Gently placing my hands behind his ears, I pulled his face next to my cheek, feeling the tickle of his whiskers. The warmth of his fur traveled through my fingertips and straight to my heart.

"Magic," I said, releasing his head, "You've made quite the artistic creation out of our beige area rug."

As I looked at the carpet I had thought was destroyed, it unexpectedly began to look beautiful. Magic's artwork reflected the voice he didn't have. It spoke to the personal challenges he struggled with every time we left him and the coping methods he used to relieve his anxiety, just like me. Great artists have drawn inspiration for their work from their own personal experiences. Magic was not that different. In that moment, I forgave him. After all, it was only an area rug, and in the end, the messed-up carpet didn't matter because I loved my dog. I wished my dad would have loved me the same way. I decided to hang up Magic's artistic rendering on the wall.

Magic rested his muzzle in my lap. His raised eyebrows jetted from side to side. In our quiet exchange, I felt a connection to him through what we had in common. We shared baggage from our pasts that had left an indelible mark on our behaviors.

"Magic, I'm making a promise to you. From now on, I'm going to try really hard not to get upset when you do something bad. I've not been very understanding in the past——you know, not handled things well, but I'm going to do better."

Magic cocked his head to the right. *"Really?"*

"My dad said hurtful things to me, so I think I know how you're feeling. If he had been more understanding, maybe a wee bit more sympathetic, that would have helped me so much. I think that's what we want from the people we love, right?"

"Yup."

Magic detested being alone and looked for ways to stave off boredom and survive separation from me in the only ways he knew how. If there was food available, he sought it out, eating whatever he could find, just like I compulsively ate desserts to alleviate the feeling of being abandoned. If Magic could locate a bathrobe, he'd find comfort in it, just like I did with my mother's house coat when I was a child.

Magic and I needed compassion from people for our lack of good coping skills. Just like I was short-sighted and judging of Magic's behavior, unaware of what had happened in his past, so was my father in shaming me about my weight gain without knowing about my experience on the cruise ship. Magic's lesson in understanding taught me that it's better to communicate your needs than to sabotage yourself. Maybe Magic had the right approach all along. When he persistently bugged me until I took him out to play Frisbee or jumped up on the bed to pester me until I pet him, I gave him attention he needed. He was a clever canine who was able to fulfill his need for love without judgment. I tried to imagine what it would be like to live in a world where human beings were less judgmental, more communicative of their needs, and a lot more loving toward each other. By example, he showed me the importance of sharing simple gestures of forgiveness.

ONE SPECIAL DOG

The familiar rhythmic panting vibrated in my ears.

"It's morning."

I had been having an argument with a store clerk about a slinky cashmere sweater that couldn't possibly cost three thousand dollars. It all faded away as I pulled up my legs and pushed down the scrunched-up comforter with my heels. With an arched back, I stretched my muscles to my toes. Wiping the sleep away, I glimpsed Magic, sitting like a Caesar, so close that a waft of his warm breath lingered. I ignored him, hoping he'd move to the end of the bed.

Was he standing guard with a watchful eye, making sure nothing happened to me during the night, or had he dozed off, dreaming of squirrels and buckets full of tennis balls? I nodded off, catching a few more precious minutes until his whiskers tickled my cheeks. A warm tongue gently brushed my eyelashes. I smiled. Feeling the velvet scruff of his neck gliding through my fingers grounded me. As I reached toward his head, I caught a silky ear in my hand. The buttery texture of Magic's ears reminded me of Bow-Wow, the stuffed dog I had as a child. Every night, I gathered the puppy's soft ear in my hand and guided it over my cheek. Comforted, I'd drift off to sleep with Bow-Wow tucked into my side.

I scooped my arm around Magic's neck, pulled him tightly to my chest, and buried my face into his fur. This was a dog who couldn't wait for me to wake up so we could start our day together. We treasured our morning routine, the quiet moments with nobody else around. The same words I said on most mornings tumbled out like I was three years old.

"I get one more day to love you. One more day to spend with you. How lucky am I?" Why didn't I wake saying the same thing to my husband and children? What was wrong with me?

Sitting down for breakfast, my thoughts were as scrambled as the two eggs with roasted bell peppers, grilled artichokes, and freshly shaved Parmesan cheese. I cut a thin slice of clove-scented pumpkin bread. Mmmmm. It tasted like heaven. Homemade pumpkin bread. A fall family favorite, the bread was made with the fresh sugar pumpkin I carved and cooked to perfection. Yes, that was one of the ways I showed my family I loved them. I spent hours in the kitchen preparing meals I knew they adored and stocked the freezers with treats, making our house the first choice for their hungry friends.

Yummy food wasn't the only way I showed my love, I rationalized. My insides wrestled with the guilt of loving Magic so deeply. Did I love him more than my husband and children? I had heard some of the rescue members say they preferred being with their dog over a human. That's because dogs have positive attitudes and love unconditionally.

No, I couldn't subscribe to a belief that my love was stronger for Magic than for my family. It was just different. A large dog breed's life span is ten to twelve years. Ten years. That's a blip in time. With the trouble he got into, I feared Magic's lifespan could be even shorter. Life is more precious when there's less time. I didn't think about Michael, Charlie, or Seth dying in ten years——or for a long time, for that matter. It was a coping mechanism that I used to use to avoid the pain of what the devastating loss of a loved one would feel like. With my husband and kids, I thought of tomorrow as being another day instead of a gift. Where was my gratitude for them? I had it for Magic.

Overwhelmed by these divergent thoughts, I pushed my chair back from the kitchen table, walked over to the couch, buried my head in a pillow and cried. Hard. I thought of the love I felt for everyone in my life, and the pain of any of them dying. Magic hated the sound of my crying, and like a mother trying to console her infant, he tried to comfort me, too. He poked his nose under my elbow and attempted to dig his way to my face. Unable to penetrate the fortress, he backed away and thunderously barked, determined to drown the muffled noise coming from the pillow.

As soon as I sat up, Magic jumped into my lap. His tongue grazed my face, wiping away tears. Although it was a small gesture, Magic's efforts comforted me. I pulled him close and hugged him. "Oh, my sweet boy."

Dogs react to whatever is happening in the moment, making them consistently, effortlessly, and entirely present. Humans, not so much. When I live in the moment, I feel happier and experience life more fully. Unfortunately, maintaining that level of awareness is a challenge in everyday life. To help me practice this discipline, I sought the guidance from chef, author, and Zen teacher, Chef Smith[1]*. His lesson was simple but profound: "When you wash the rice, wash the rice." Meaning, if you concentrate on what you are doing in that moment, it will be powerful, transformational, even a task as mundane as washing rice. Chef Smith inspired me to practice mindfulness through meditation, but nobody was more skilled at bringing me into the present than Magic.

One morning, while Magic and I were sharing pillow time, I contemplated whether or not to take him out for a game of Frisbee in the preserve. I hesitated, remembering the day when coyotes lured Magic away from the game, drew him into the desert, and attacked him. I watched in the distance as the two lean-bodied coyotes pinned him to the ground and bit his back leg. There was nothing I could do but yell as he fought for his life. He freed himself and limped back to me with a bloodied hip and flattened ears. But as traumatic as the incident had been for me, Magic recovered and appeared to be unaffected. If there was an opportunity to chase after a Frisbee, he was all in, always right in the moment.

People, other dogs, or food didn't matter when our Frisbee games started. Magic's teeth chattered with excitement as he beat the grass with his front paws, snorting and barking, impatient for the first toss. When I drew back my arm to wind up for the throw, he bolted down the field, body half twisted to catch the first sight of the red saucer flying through the air. He'd check his speed, sprinting if necessary, preparing to make the leap for the perfect catch.

Magic's passion for his Frisbee was admired by many who saw him. Bystanders would stop, commenting on his determination to catch every throw and his tenacity in repeatedly dropping the disc at my feet in anticipation of the whole process beginning again. When we played the game, I didn't think of anything else but tossing the saucer and watching Magic fly through the air. My worries, chore list, job responsibilities, and anxieties fell away when we were on the field together. Some days I wasn't sure who enjoyed the game more. We were five hundred percent in the moment.

Nothing was going to stop Magic's daily game of Frisbee. His enthusiasm was entertaining and his energy contagious. Weather permitting, we'd head out to the preserve every day after his breakfast. One particularly windy day, I waited until the afternoon, thinking the gusts would die down. By one o'clock, Magic was banging the closet door with his paw, impatient for me to produce the toy. His persistence won out.

Frisbees don't cooperate in the wind. No matter what strategy I tried, it was no surprise the saucer veered into a bush several times. Magic, determined to make the catch, crashed head-first into the leaves. I was ready to say game over when I heard a woman screaming in the distance. "Magic, come." He trotted over to me, dropping the Frisbee at my feet.

"How about another toss?"

"Magic, sit."

"Why?"

"Quiet," I said, reaching out to snap on his leash.

"Help! I need help!" A panicked woman came running out of the preserve. "Please, help me!" she shouted. "I've lost my daughter. We were up there." She pointed to the mountains high above the preserve. My gaze followed her gesture to take in the sprawling landscape of rocks and cacti.

"I took my eyes off her for one minute. She's only four. I can't find her," she said in between sobs. "Look, my friend is still up there."

The fear in her voice reminded me of what I had experienced with Seth when he was four years old and went missing in a department store. But there was no time to think about that. Her outburst brought me back into focus.

"What's your daughter's name?"

"Her name is Morgan. I'm Sherry."

"Did you call 911?"

"Yes, they're on their way."

"I'm Lauren."

Magic barked, and then bumped me on the leg with his chest. I looked at him. "What? What, Magic?" He bumped me again, trying to get my attention. I scowled at him. "No, we're not playing Frisbee anymore."

Magic turned to Sherry and pressed his nose into her stomach repeatedly. It gave me an idea. "Do you have anything that smells like Morgan?"

Sherry pulled out a pink jacket that had been tucked in her backpack. "I have this." She handed the coat to me. I put the material in front of Magic's nose. He breathed in the scent.

"Let's go. You lead the way," I said to Sherry. "Tell me when we're close to where you were standing when you last saw Morgan. Maybe Magic can track her."

Sherry, Magic, and I ran through the preserve, crossing washes, scrambling up rocks, and dodging cactus on the way. We could see her friend yelling in the distance. Magic, still tethered to a leash, pulled like a team of horses.

When we reached her friend, I pulled the jacket out of my hand and stretched it between my arms. Dipping my hands in Magic's direction, I gave him another chance to sniff the material.

"Let's see if he can find your little girl."

Sherry turned to her friend. "Stay here in case Morgan shows up." Her friend nodded.

"Okay, Magic." I unsnapped the leash. "Go find Morgan." He bolted. His tail shot straight into the air. His ears were up and his eyes forward.

Magic traipsed down rock faces, at times dipping out of view. He stopped and pawed at the dirt, sending a cloud into the air before darting ahead. I could barely keep up with his feverish pace. How far could this child have gone?

Magic started barking in short, excited outbursts. I could see the tip of his tail moving rapidly. I heard Sherry panting behind me, trying to catch up.

"I think he found her!" I yelled back to her.

"Oh, please, dear God."

I heard a child crying. After making one more turn on the rocky path, I saw Magic and Morgan wedged between a bush and a rock. Magic was standing guard over the frightened child. Before I could announce I had found them, Sherry ran past me, jumped into the rocky area, and lifted Morgan into her arms. Both were wailing so hard I could barely hear Magic's barks.

"Magic, good boy, good boy!" I told him. I reached over, giving him pats on the head and plastering his face with kisses. "I knew you could do it. You're my hero."

"Hero?"

I looked over at Sherry, who was still crying, sitting in the dirt rocking Morgan back and forth. The two were so tightly intertwined they looked like one person. I snapped on Magic's leash and walked away to give them space.

Minutes later a firefighter and his crew called out to us. "I'm Sam. Are you the people who called 911 for a lost child? Have you located the child yet?"

"We found her!" I said, pointing in Morgan's direction. I directed Sam and his crew to the mother and child still entangled in a ball.

"Sherry, we're responding to your 911 call. We'd like to check Morgan out." Sherry continued to rock Morgan.

"Sherry? We're here to help. We're responding to your 911 call. We'd like to check Morgan out." She released the child.

"Sorry, yes, of course. I'm so…" Sherry's eyes filled with tears.

Sam and the rest of the firefighters evaluated Morgan, taking her vitals, checking her for cuts and other injuries. I overheard Sam call the alarm room to cancel the remainder of the assignment. "Yes, the child has been located and is well. No additional resources are needed. Refused further treatment. Hold engine thirty-eight. Place remainder of assignment as available."

I felt lightheaded. For the first time in what seemed like hours, I could breathe normally. Magic barked, unable to contain his excitement with all the activity. Sam walked toward us.

"Are they going to be okay?" I asked.

"Yes, thanks to you and your dog, they're going to be fine."

"Oh man, really scary. I didn't know if we'd find her——whether she'd …"

"Hey, it's okay. Let's get you and your dog some water. What's his name?"

"Magic."

He pulled out a bottle, poured some water into a makeshift bowl for Magic, and handed me the rest.

"We're grateful you were able to find Morgan."

"I wish I could take the credit, but Magic's the one who did it."

"Yes, he sniffed her out. I'm impressed." Sam squatted on his knees. "Good job, Magic," he said, patting him on the head and running his hand under his ears for a long scratch. "You're one special dog."

"That was fun. Can we do it again?"

Voices emerged from behind the rocks as two of the firefighters flanked Sherry and Morgan, helping them traverse the rocky path down the mountain. Seeing mother and daughter holding hands was heartwarming. When we arrived in the parking lot, Sherry walked over and hugged me.

"How can I ever thank you for helping me find Morgan?" she said. "I'll be forever grateful for what you did for us. Thank you, thank you, thank you."

As I pulled away, my hands caught her fingers, still dusty from the dirt. "You're welcome," I said, squeezing her palms, "but the credit goes to Magic. He's the one who did all the work."

"Oh yes, that's true! Magic will always be my favorite dog on the planet. I want to drop off a juicy bone for him." She looked at Magic, who cocked his head, suddenly taking great interest in what she was saying.

"Did someone say bone?"

I looked down at Morgan, who had a hand on Magic's neck. "I see she has a few scratches, but there's nothing serious, right?"

"She's fine, physically. Right now, I have my little girl and nothing else matters." She paused, looking over at Magic with loving eyes. "And thanks, again," she called back to me, walking toward her car. "Thanks for sharing your incredible dog with us."

I looked at Magic. "C'mon, boy, I think it's time we head back to the house. I'm wiped out. We'll continue the Frisbee game tomorrow."

"What about my bone?"

Later that night, gathered around the dinner table for Thai pork potstickers with coconut curry sauce and an Asian mango salsa. I told the family about Magic saving the day. How Magic, using his perceptive sniffer and unrelenting drive, found a lost child on a desert mountain preserve. I was feeling giddy, proud of Magic, and thrilled by his charisma and tenacious personality.

"Mom, you think Magic was a hero today, don't you?" Seth asked.

"Well, what else would you call him?" I chided. "That's what the firefighters and the mom called him. If you could have seen him today in action, you'd agree, our Magic pulled off a phenomenal deed. You know, you probably don't remember, but I had a similar experience of losing you when you were the exact same age. In a department store, combing through a clothing rack for a dress, you vanished. I took my eye off you for a minute, and you disappeared. I frantically searched the neighboring racks looking for you before asking a store clerk to call security. Ten minutes later, a security guard found you nestled under a rack in the designer dress department. Believe me when I tell you the experience of losing a child is agonizing, truly gut wrenching, and one that no mother can ever forget. After what I went though, I think anyone who finds a lost child is a hero."

Michael smiled. "Magic can be a good dog, sometimes."

"Okay," Seth said. "I guess you're right. Magic was a hero today."

Magic was a hero. The words echoed in my ears.

---

1. * This character and quotes are from Edward Espe Brown

THE RIGHT CHOICE

A warmth spread through me every time I thought about Magic's rescue on the preserve. I was proud of him for being able to spring into action without hesitation in that chaotic moment. My hero didn't gloat about what had happened. He was his same old self: quick to excite and ready for the next adventure. I looked at him differently after the incident because he wasn't just a regular dog. He was a superhero. I thought of buying him a red cape but settled for a red bandana instead. I called my friends to recount the story, beaming every time I had the chance to talk about Magic's dynamic rescue. The subject of my star canine's new-found skill was captivating dinner conversation.

"I still can't believe Magic did something right for a change," Seth said, dipping his Vietnamese spring roll into a red curry peanut sauce.

Charlie looked at Magic trying to nose into his lap. "Just because you did something amazing doesn't mean you are entitled to more treats."

"Treats? Where?" Magic ducked under the table, hoping food had dropped. Some things would never change, including the idea that he would ever settle down and be a normally functioning dog.

I thought leaving his early kennel experiences in the rear-view mirror and providing a stable home would change his eccentric personality. But as the months ticked by, that notion turned out to be incorrect. Despite the loving, attentive household, routine feeding schedule, and structured daily exercise, he was still extremely high-spirited. No amount of trying to will the situation to be different was going to change reality. His renewable energy on most days proved exasperating and time consuming, requiring new and creative ways of thinking about how to incorporate rigorous exercise without exhausting or wounding myself in the process. Even more, this job required planning to avoid consequences such as a spine killing aerobic workout in the reckless pursuit of simply securing a harness before departing the house.

Through all the craziness, I started to worry that living out his life as a family pet seemed restrictive and confining for a dog whose energy level and temperament might have been better served else-where. I imagined him living on a farm, having the freedom to chase sheep and whipping through fields of wheat, nose in the air, the grains tickling his nostrils. I could see him following the farmhands on horseback through fields of blue, yellow, and purple wildflowers and lush, green pastures, watching the chickens in the coop scratch the ground looking for grubs. Then I envisioned a horse kicking him, delivering a fatal blow to the head because he ran too closely behind it. There had to be other options, but what were they? Who could I call? While contemplating my next move, I happened to open an email from Magic's adoption group. The organization was hosting a weekend meet and greet event at a local pet store. The event provided the perfect opportunity for me to discuss my concerns with the volunteers. I couldn't wait for Saturday to arrive.

I smiled as I walked toward the entrance of the store, remem-bering the first time I experienced a get together like this one while shopping for a toy for Maddie. Today, there were seven fosters who brought their Labradors to the three-hour event. In between the waves of potential adopters showing up to play and interact with all the pooches, we had a few minutes to share stories about the rescues we had made part of our families.

Nobody could compete with my detailed, animated account of the hilarious but daunting exploits Magic rained on our family. After the laughter died down, Galvin, an older gentleman with a beard, cowboy boots, and jeans, put his hand up.

"Have you thought about researching an agility program that might help with his behavioral issues?" he asked. "They set up courses that test a dog's physical and mental ability using obstacles like tunnels and weave polls. The experience is like a canine Olympics." Galvin paused. "Or maybe you could look into a SAR program. A dog that does search and rescue is trained to track and seek out people who have gone missing. When it finds the person, the dog alerts their handler. Every search is a different job assignment——it's hard physical and mental work to find their victims, but it's great for dogs that need more stimulation."

"Magic, a candidate for a search and rescue program? I don't know. Aren't those dogs professionally trained to find people in dangerous situations like avalanches?"

"Yes, but with everything you've said about Magic, I think it would be a perfect fit."

Galvin's comment weighed heavily on my mind the remainder of the weekend. When I brought the subject up to Michael, he suggested talking to Dr. Walker, our accomplished Phoenix veterinarian, who had been giving us advice about how to manage Magic's behavioral challenges. He knew first-hand the bizarre stories I lived through with Magic. He was a good person to consult because during office visits he routinely took extra time to listen to my concerns and offered unbiased and experienced advice. I appreciated his support and empathy, feeling he understood how difficult it was to deal with Magic's antics.

I called and made an appointment, opting to talk to Dr. Walker in person rather than discussing the matter over the phone. On the way to clinic, Magic's whine escalated into a full-blown bark. *Are we going to the park?*

"Magic, calm down. Sit."

"Can't sit. Too excited."

Pulling into the parking lot, he came unglued.

"Where's the park?"

I opened the door a crack and reached in to grab his leash. Magic pushed the door open with his chest and leaped several feet out of the car, taking me with him. I lunged forward as my neck snapped backward. "Magic, stop pulling." I took a big breath and walked toward the entrance.

"Tank's already empty, let's go." I steered him to the check-in area. The office staff recorded his weight and whisked us off to a room. A vet tech took Magic's vitals and said the doctor would be in shortly. Magic panted and paced across the tile floor.

"This place again?"

Minutes later, Dr. Walker entered the exam room. "Hi, Lauren, how's Magic doing these days? The vet tech said the reason for Magic's visit is not about his physical health."

"Yes, that's right. He's good in that department. It's about his mental health," I said, hesitantly. "We haven't had a major mishap in a while, but, as you know, that could change at any moment." Dr. Walker ran his hand over Magic's head and then placed a stethoscope on his chest.

"I'm worried Magic pulls these crazy stunts because he's bored." I took a breath, then continued. "I think he needs a job. I got some validation of that at an adoption event sponsored by our rescue. One of our Desert Labrador Retriever Rescue volunteers had an interesting reaction to the stories I told about Magic. I had them laughing so hard. You know how hilarious my tales have been." Dr. Walker smiled. "But one guy must have been a bit dumbfounded by what I said because he suggested I research an agility club or a search and rescue program for Magic. I hadn't thought about anything like that and now I can't get the idea out of my head. What do you think?"

Dr. Walker's lips curled into a gentle smile, and with a warm tone of voice he said, "I think either one of those options might be a right fit for Magic. I know Ted, the president of the local search and rescue association. They have an exceptional staff. I'd be happy to call them on your behalf."

As we chatted about how Magic might benefit from the training and structure, I sank into the chair, thinking that the search and rescue organization could hold the most promise for Magic's rare qualities. Loud noises did not deter him, and although he was friendly to everyone he met, he also operated independently. If there was a job to be done, action won out over pats on the back and scratches under the chin. I witnessed his caretaking skills when I had accidents and knew he could run on pure adrenaline for hours at a time without losing focus or taking a break. He had already demonstrated an innate ability to find a human using his physical strength and agility to navigate a rugged mountain preserve. His Olympic sniffer, undying loyalty, and selfless acts attested that he would sacrifice his life to save someone.

After professional training and certifications, he would be able to use his boundless energy to track missing people in various situations, performing a skill that could save a human life. I sighed, thinking that a dog whose life had hung on a thread because of limited resources at the shelter could be responsible for saving more people like Morgan.

"Can we go now?"

Magic's booming bark jolted me to sit up straight in the chair. "Yes, I do think he could make a difference doing search and rescue," I said with confidence. "Would you call Ted and let him know I'm interested in the program?"

"I'd be happy to do that. I've seen Magic, what, probably ten times, and based on everything you've told me and how he acts every time he's in the office, I think he has the personality and ability to do that kind of work."

I thought I had the whole situation figured out. But that triumphant feeling disappeared when Dr. Walker asked, "How do you feel about surrendering him?"

"What? Give him up?" That was not what I expected to hear. I stared at him.

"That's a requirement of the program. You have to turn him over to the professionals to do the training."

I half listened to the words trailing out of his mouth because of the noise rattling in the back of my head. He talked about the other dogs he had referred to the program and Ted's exceptional leadership, but I tuned out many of the details. Sensing my detachment, Dr. Walker scooted toward me on his stool and looked into my eyes.

"Do you think Magic needs more stimulation and a setting where he can use his energy for the greater good?"

I nervously rubbed my hands together. "I haven't been totally honest about why I'm asking for your opinion. A week ago, Magic found a little girl who was lost in the preserve. We were out playing Frisbee when a mother asked for our help in finding her four-year-old. I couldn't believe it when Magic sprang into action and found her in record time. I have been thinking about what happened, wondering if his calling is to be in search and rescue."

But there it was, the idea of surrendering Magic to a program that would better meet his needs. I finally had the courage to take the step that would result in my losing him, a subject I had not even thought about. It was a place where denial and grief meshed, where I had to confront the prospect that he wouldn't be with me anymore. I pulled out a tissue, dabbing my nose.

With rolled back ears and a motionless tail, Magic walked over, sat in front of me and gently placed a paw on my knee.

"You're going to give me up? Really?"

"Are you okay? I know how much you care about this dog. Here's more tissues." He handed me the box. "That's an incredible story. If he did that without any prior training, he must be a natural born rescue dog."

He paused, seeing my bleary eyes. "But I see how upset you are with the thought of giving him up. Take some time and think about it. There's a lot to consider. Call me if you want to talk." The vet stood, gave Magic a pat on the head, and extended his hand to me. "Nobody knows what's best for Magic better than you do."

I thanked him and walked out of the office in silence.

There was that familiar theme. The idea that, as his dog mom, only I knew what was in Magic's best interest. But what was in Magic's best interest was not necessarily what I wanted. On our way home I glanced in the rear-view mirror, scanning Magic's face for answers only I could decipher. I decided to put off the conversation with the president of the search and rescue organization, even though I knew that Magic, almost two years of age, had to be evaluated and accepted before he was too old for the program. Despite the temporary relief I felt from making that decision, my conflicted internal dialogue continued. I made up excuses for not calling Ted. Whenever Michael and the kids asked me if I was going to turn him over to the organization, I downplayed Magic's strengths to convince everyone he'd never be accepted.

When I envisioned signing the surrender papers and turning over his leash to another person, my complex range of emotions left me barely able to breathe. How would I feel if I never saw him again? The guilt haunted me. I felt my indecision was compromising Magic's life, knowing how much he would love that job. Why would I deny him the opportunity to live a better quality of life? I cursed myself for being so selfish, for not making my prime consideration what would be best for Magic. The argument wouldn't leave me alone.

Over the next few months, I suffered bouts of fear every time I picked up the phone to contact the organization. My sweating hands were barely able to grip the phone. I added coward to the description of my personality traits when I couldn't bear to complete the call. I promised myself if Magic showed no promise of settling down and still needed more stimulation than our family could provide, I wouldn't hang up.

Three weeks later, Magic gave me a sign. While the whole family was out for dinner on my birthday, Magic celebrated, too, entertaining himself by ingesting two cups of cocoa powder, resulting in a trip to the veterinary hospital to induce vomiting. This dog needed a job where foraging and consuming copious amounts of dangerous foods would not be an option. I knew how hazardous chocolate could be when ingested by dogs. *Lauren, take a hard look at what just happened. Why did I leave the cocoa powder container wedged behind the dish drainer? What was my rationale in thinking he couldn't grab it? He's so agile. What's worse is that the whole mess could have been avoided if the chocolate had been stored in the pantry. This was another big mistake—— one that could have cost him his life. How could I live with myself if he died because of my negligence?*

Wracked with guilt, I decided to give him up. I knew the right person to call after what had happened. Ted, the president of SAR, made it easy to share my journey with Magic and summarize why I thought his characteristics and energy would drive him to complete a mission. A lump forming in my throat slowed down my ability to ask the question.

"Ted, do you think Magic could be a candidate for the organization?" I held my breath waiting for his response, not fully prepared for what the answer might be. I could hear him shuffling papers.

"I have his application, but I'll need to review it before I get back to you. He'd be a great candidate based on what you've already told me about him."

"If Magic is selected, can you tell me how long he'd be part of your organization?"

"Most of our dogs actively participate in the program for six years and then retire at age eight."

"After he's retired, could he come back to live with us?"

"It all depends. There are several factors to consider. We would make that decision at the time of his retirement."

"Oh, I see. I was hoping he could live out his senior days with us. The whole family loves him so much. You know, it's hard giving up a dog. If we knew he was coming back to us it might make it easier." There was silence at the other end of the phone. "Okay. Then I'll wait to hear back from you. Thank you."

"Thank you, Lauren. I'll be in touch."

The next two days I spoiled Magic, giving him extra tummy rubs and long walks in the mountain preserve. Had I made the right decision to call the organization? I second guessed myself several times a day, wondering what my life would be like without Magic. When Ted's number came up on my phone, I anxiously picked it up.

"Hello, Lauren, this is Ted from SAR. Thanks for entrusting us with the selection process for your dog. I enjoyed our conversation about Magic. He seems like he's a remarkable dog, even if he is challenging."

"That's true, but I think that more than anything, he needs a job. I haven't been able to do that for him."

There was a long pause. "I've reviewed his file and discussed his profile with my staff. He has the qualities we're looking for. We would need to begin his training right away so he's not too old to begin the year of intensive training he would need to be certified. We'll need your answer in the next two weeks."

THE UNTHINKABLE

Maybe my desire to keep Magic came from self-interest, but who could blame me for not wanting to part with him? The crazy pooch had wiggled his way into being a central part of my life. I scooped Magic's face into my hands, bringing his nose inches from mine.

"We have to make a decision about whether or not to turn you over to a search organization. Ahhhh, sweet boy, I love you," I said, pulling him closer to kiss his head. "I don't know what to do, Magic. We only have one more week to think about it."

Magic stepped back, looked me in the eyes and cocked his ears.

Whether I was thinking about Magic, childhood pals, college roommates, or close friends, I felt the same way about all of them. I couldn't bear the thought of their not being in my life, knowing how significant their friendships were to me. I fostered those relationships, appreciating my friends' quirks and character flaws as they accepted mine. Sharing our true selves and building trust, we cemented a bond of enduring affection in the process. My personal relationships were central to my existence.

Magic differed from my human friends, of course, being a canine, but that didn't stop me from forming an emotional attachment to him. His loyalty and abiding devotion showed he was not only invested in me, but in my family as well.

Over the next week, our family conversations danced around making a decision. Our list, factoring in what would be best for Magic and the family, changed daily. The conversation droned on because no one wanted to be the first to decide. We were locked in a stalemate. That was until the unthinkable happened.

One hot afternoon, only days before I had to make the call to the SAR president, I was hanging out with Magic and Maddie by the pool, when we heard loud yips and high-pitched barks coming from the front yard. Magic, hearing the commotion, darted to the front gate and pasted his nose between the wood slats, trying to catch a glimpse of the action. He pawed at the base of the gate with numerous jabs, trying to break free.

"Magic, come. What're you doing?" Before I could grab his collar, he backed up five feet and bolted full speed toward our stucco wall. I was stunned as our athlete scaled the seven-foot structure effortlessly, landing in our neighbor's yard. He dashed to their gate and pushed it open, exiting onto the street. I raced over to our gate and fumbled with the lock. Pushing it open, I only caught a glimpse of two medium-sized brown dogs sprinting down the block at lightning speed. Panicked, I watched the two instigators disappear around the corner, Magic right on their heels in a high-speed chase.

I ran after them through the neighborhood, calling Magic's name, but was unable to keep up after several blocks. My legs felt like rubber, forcing me to jog and then slow to a hurried walk. I peered down the street, hoping to see Magic waiting for me, but he had disappeared. My heart pounded, each beat louder and faster. Knowing he had no awareness of cars pushed me into panic mode.

"Magic! Magic!" I bellowed. Where could he have gone, and how did I end up in an unfamiliar neighborhood? There had to be a better way to continue the search than on foot. As I jogged back to the house, a new plan emerged. I burst through the door, grabbed my phone, and called Michael at work.

"Honey——Magic——he chased a dog, I've been looking——he's gone. I'm losing it."

"What? You've got to slow down. What happened?"

I filled Michael in on the details and asked what else I should do.

"Call Animal Services and file a lost dog report," he answered immediately. "I'll post the info on social media. Give me the hotline number for Magic's rescue. I'll call them and let them know what happened. I'll be home as quick as I can. Let's wait to tell the kids."

"I will, but I feel totally helpless. I don't know why I didn't think to call Animal Services. What's wrong with me?"

"You're frantic. Everything's going to be okay."

"Call me when you get to the house. I've got to go back out to look for him."

I hung up the phone and tried to focus on next steps. While making the call to Animal Services, I rummaged through my purse, digging, throwing the contents everywhere, looking for car keys. Why had he run away? Magic was gone. As I rushed out to the car, I remembered stories I had heard about rescue dogs having a predisposition to run away. I quickly dismissed the idea that Magic might be one of those dogs. The voice in my head shouted at me. *Bad decision! Big mistake not turning him over to the search and rescue organization. Why didn't we decide sooner? All of this could have been avoided.* My mind spit out random reasons for his disappearance. *Magic was bored. He needed a job. He wanted a new adventure. He didn't get enough exercise.* I struggled to swallow the lump in my throat. I climbed into the car, backed out of the driveway, and drove around the block.

As the minutes ticked by, the chances of finding him lessened. Although he had been chipped and wore a collar embroidered with my phone number, I worried for his life. We lived near major city streets with cars traveling at high speeds. He would be defenseless if he tried to cross a busy roadway.

I tried to make myself feel better. He had many choices. He could find another person or family to befriend, spot a game of Frisbee to join, or catch up with the dogs and wrestle his newest playmates. I tried to predict what he would do, but in reality, I had no clue what the thought process of a dog like Magic would be. He'd been gone for twenty minutes. I had visions of him lying in the street, bleeding, a car with a dented fender, a driver hunched over his body.

"He's going to be okay; he's going to be okay," I chanted, repeating the mantra out loud to stop from thinking the worst.

I stopped people and asked if anyone had seen a black lab. No one had. Suddenly, as I stared down the block, I spotted a black dog. I found him! Ohhhhhh, that's him! I jammed on the brakes, put the car in park, threw the door open, and jumped out of my seat.

It wasn't Magic. Where is my dog? I drove around until Michael called to let me know he was at the house. Looking at my watch, I saw an hour had elapsed, even though it felt like two minutes. I turned the car around and sped home. Relieved to see Michael's car in the driveway, I ran to the house.

"Michael! Michael!" I shouted.

Michael opened the door and flung his arms around me.

"I can't find him. He's gone. What are we going to do?"

Michael waited for me to regain my composure. "Listen, you've been out looking for a while. It's my turn. I'm going to change clothes and head out. Why don't you wait for the kids to get home from school? You didn't text them, did you?"

"No, I didn't. I'll wait for them." Maddie walked over and rubbed her nose into my knee.

"Honey, look at Maddie," Michael said. "She needs some love right now. Give her some attention. It would be good for both of you. I'll be back after I change."

"Hi, Maddie-girl," I said, reaching out to pet her neck. "Are you going to keep me company until the boys come home? C'mon, let's go sit on the couch." Maddie followed closely behind.

"Where are you, hon?" Michael called.

"In the family room."

Michael appeared around the corner and blew me a kiss. "I'll call you with any news."

"Thanks," I mumbled. Maddie jumped on the sofa and flopped

down on my lap. "What are you doing? You're too big to be a lap dog." She turned her head to look at me. My eyes caught her gaze.

"Where's your brother? Why hasn't he come back?" A tear rolled off the edge of my cheek and dropped onto her ear.

"Maddie, I'm so upset," I whispered, hugging her around the neck, pulling her close to my chest. As I slowly released my arms, her head nestled back into my lap. With an outstretched hand I gently floated my fingertips down her earlobe. The softness of her fur comforted me. *Lauren, try to keep it together. But how can I do that when I'm feeling frantic? Take a deep breath.* I gently moving her paws to the side. "The boys will be home soon. I need to grab a tissue from the bedroom before they get here. I don't want them to think I'm falling apart."

When only Maddie greeted Charlie and Seth at the door, they hustled into the kitchen, throwing their backpacks on the counter.

"Hey, Mom, is Magic with you?" Charlie yelled.

I walked out of the bedroom, holding back tears.

"Where's Magic? Is he in the hospital again?"

I reached out to the boys for a group hug as a tear rolled down my face. Their warm embrace gave me the strength to continue. "No, he's not in the hospital."

"Then, where is he?" Charlie asked. "Magic's always at the door when we come home."

"He's...he's... not here. I don't know where he is. He jumped over our wall and disappeared."

"What? I don't understand," Seth said. "He ran away? What happened?" Charlie and Seth shook their heads as I shared the details of Magic's disappearance.

Charlie looked at Seth. "I'm going to look for him. You coming with me?"

"Yeah, we should use our bikes."

"You might run into Dad——he left a half hour ago to look, too."

After the boys pulled their bikes out of the garage, they barreled back into the house. "We're going to start at the park and end up at the canals," Seth said. "Be back by dinner."

"Okay," I said, handing them water bottles. "You have your phones in case I need to call you?" They reached in their pockets and waved them at me. They flew out of the driveway, focused on their mission.

As the hours ticked away and the sun started to set, I worried about the boys riding around the neighborhood with no lights. I paced the tile in the kitchen, burning off nervous energy and waiting for the phone to ring. When everyone came home looking disappointed, I knew they hadn't found him.

The family assembled for a dinner of leftover lasagna even though nobody was hungry. Placing thick slices of garlic bread under the broiler, I stared off into the distance, worried I might never see Magic again.

"Mom! There's smoke coming from the oven."

"Oh, no." I pulled out the smoldering bread and placed it in the sink. Charlie and Seth excused themselves from the table to escape the tension.

"We're not hungry right now. Maybe after we do some homework we'll feel like eating," Seth mumbled.

Michael put his arms around me. "Magic will come back. I know he will."

"I don't know. He's been gone for hours."

"Don't jump to conclusions. We can't do anything more tonight. Let's try not to think about it. How about turning on the TV?"

"I'm so heartbroken I can hardly breathe. I have no idea where he is, if he's safe, if something happened to him——I love that dog way too much."

"Okay, then let's do something. Let's go for a walk. Maybe that will help."

"Good idea," I said. "We can look for Magic."

Michael and I walked for an hour that night, wandering down side streets and alleys. Disappointed and thirsty, we returned to the house. Seth and Charlie opened the door hoping to see Magic.

"We didn't find him."

"Do you think he's dead, Mom?" Seth asked.

"We're not going to think about that now."

Charlie reached out to hug me. I sobbed from the combined grief of all four of us. Everyone followed. We clung to each other, building a fortress to shield ourselves from the heartache of losing a loved one. I wanted to roll back the clock to the time before Magic had leaped the fence. If only he hadn't heard the two dogs, if only the wall had been built higher, if only I had taken the car first instead of running after him.

Michael distributed tissues and pulled one for himself. He placed his arm around my waist and said, "I'm going to get us some water." The boys followed us into the kitchen and sat at the table.

"I love Magic so much," Charlie said. "He's part of the family. Why would he run away?"

Seth looked up. "I'm worried about him, too. How could he leave? I know I've complained about his barking and all the crazy stuff he does, but there's no other dog like him. He's our dog. He belongs with us."

Charlie nodded. "Why did we talk about giving him to a SAR program?"

I closed my eyes, rocking back and forth. "Oh, sweetie, Magic knows how much we love him. And we know how much we love Magic and believe that he's our dog. But remember, he was a stray when the county shelter found him. We have no idea why he was out on the streets. The rescue told me they don't know why re-homed dogs run away, but sometimes that happens."

Michael handed me a glass of water and pulled out a chair. "We've got to stay positive. We might get a call from the city shelter or maybe we'll hear from Magic's rescue organization. One of the volunteers said they would post information on social media. He's chipped and has a collar with Mom's phone number. There's a good chance somebody will pick him up and call us."

Charlie's sniffling was the only sound in the room. Michael handed him a tissue. Were the boys as afraid as I was to hope that Magic would be found? I didn't say anything, fearful of overshadowing Michael's upbeat comments.

Nervously glancing at my watch, I was relieved to see it was ten o'clock. "It's getting late. I'm going to get ready for bed. I think we should all do that."

The truth of the matter was the weight of my sadness left me unable to cope. I hugged the kids like I never wanted to let them go and then pointed them toward their bedrooms. As I headed for the bathroom, the sound of sniffling noses floated from the other room.

I climbed into bed, wondering if there was any chance of getting to sleep. I thought back to the sleepless nights when we first brought Magic home. Oh, I'd give anything to be able to experience that eccentric dog again. I picked up a book and started reading, hoping to quiet my stomach. When the lines on the book blurred, I reached over, turned off the light, and buried my face in the pillow.

DOG OF MY HEART

I had a dream that Magic was at the foot of the bed. I shot up and reached down to skim the end of the mattress. The space was empty, cold from the draft of the air conditioner. Dark sky filtered through the window. I wondered if I should dress and start looking for Magic. When I glanced at the clock, the digital display read three am. Unable to sleep, I tiptoed out of bed and went to the bathroom to pee. Before returning to the bedroom, I caught a glimpse of myself in the mirror. I leaned in closer, staring at my image, and there was Magic staring back, my soulmate and my catalyst to see things clearer about myself and be a better person. That's what soulmates do for each other. I couldn't have known when we first adopted him, that Magic would help me to enjoy the simple wonders that today has to offer, to appreciate the people who mean the most to me, and to love them with an open heart. He reminded me to tuck away special memories of loved ones because life has an expiration date. I thought about his enthusiasm for all things in life. Whether a Frisbee game, a treat, a ride in the car, or a homecoming, he was always his true self, kindhearted and giving.

Magic's free spirit beckoned me to seize new adventures. His fearless outlook taught me to be carefree. A part of me enjoyed living vicariously through his impulsive spirit and feeling alive in the moment. Having a dog like Magic gave me the excuse to revisit my younger years, when the rush of adrenaline, the absence of responsibility, and spontaneous joy made me feel like a child, wild and free. I was impetuous in my youth, taking risks because the adventure was too great to resist, just like Magic. Every time I looked at him, I was looking at a mirror image. We had always been and would continue to be one and the same.

I knew there had to be a reason why I had brought this crazy dog home. Now the answers emerged like a jigsaw puzzle that I had been working on for a long time.

I helped Magic overcome his traumatic past and live life to its full potential, but the journey wasn't easy for either of us. Our relationship had to endure bouts of emotional and physical pain, frustration, and trust issues. The distressing experiences, like consuming two cups of cocoa powder and nearly drowning in the pool, caused me agonizing pain for loving a dog that I wasn't sure would survive. But it was in those moments that I realized how to be brave and muster the courage to think of death as a part of life I couldn't control.

What was the right thing to do now? Could I offer Magic the life he needed here with us? His brushes with death gave me the courage to let go of control. *Am I supposed to let go of Magic now, too, let him fulfill his potential with SAR? Do I have the strength to make a decision and live with the consequences?* Either way I was risking the pain of making the wrong choice and never forgiving myself.

As I continued to stare in the mirror, I was torn between waves of heart-felt gratitude for Magic's gifts and the grief of losing the dog of my heart. It didn't make sense to me. *Lauren, if Magic loved the family, why did he run off? Why hadn't he come back?* A wave of sadness washed over me. I left the bathroom and slipped under the covers, finding comfort in Michael's snores.

The next morning, gathered around the breakfast table, the boys didn't ask for their usual breakfast of eggs, bacon, and toast.

"I don't feel like going to school," Charlie said as he poured a glass of milk. "Can't I stay home and go with you to look for Magic?"

"Yeah, it's going to be hard for me to concentrate on anything today," Seth added.

"Listen, I can't have you two missing classes. The teachers wouldn't take too kindly to the excuse. I'll keep you posted on what's happening. I love you guys so much." The boys and I embraced in a three-way hug before they slowly shuffled outside to the carpool, hanging their heads.

"Honey, would you like me to help look for him? I'm thinking like the kids," Michael said. "I'm not going to be able to concentrate at work, either."

I looked over at Michael lovingly. "I could use the support. I didn't get much sleep last night."

"Let me get on my sneakers and we'll go."

I collected Magic's leash, a couple water bottles, a handful of treats, and his favorite ball. Setting out on foot, we stopped at the end of the driveway. I was overwhelmed, having no idea where to begin looking.

"We can start out together, but at some point, I think we should split up. That way we can cover more ground," Michael said.

"Good idea. Let's walk together for a couple blocks."

We paused every fifty feet to look in people's backyards and down side streets, hoping to catch sight of our dog. We stopped random individuals, asking them if they had seen a black lab running loose. Nobody had seen one. Knowing Magic's athleticism, he could have run miles from our neighborhood. My heart pounded harder. Michael and I walked for ten more minutes, neither one of us wanting to share our feelings.

"I think it's time to split up. I'm going to head south. I'll see you at the park in forty-five minutes."

"Okay, I'll canvas this road and then circle back to meet you. I've got my cell phone. Call me if you find him. Oh, and here, take your water bottle." He hugged me, then walked toward the canal path. I felt the morning heat radiate from the crunchy gravel. The temperature felt like one hundred degrees at eight o'clock in the morning. A stray dog couldn't last long without water. I picked up my step. Every time I passed someone with a leashed dog, I felt a pang of jealousy. I walked for a while before stopping under the shade of a mesquite tree to wipe off my sunglasses and take a drink of water. I looked at my watch. I needed to meet Michael in twenty minutes.

When I arrived at the park, my heart fell when Michael approached me with no sign of Magic.

I sighed. "He's gone. I know it. Something happened to him." I covered my face, trying to block out everything. For the first time, I was truly afraid Magic was dead.

Michael held my fingers gently, inching me toward him. "I know," he whispered. He pulled me in for a hug. I held on, wanting the comfort of his embrace.

"Lauren," he said, pulling away and looking me in the eye, "I know this is hard for you. It's gut-wrenching for me, too. But I'm not ready to give up. I don't think you're ready to give up, either. We have to keep the faith."

"No, I don't want to give up, but I don't think we're getting anywhere by walking around the neighborhood. We need do something different, figure out a new plan. What do you think?"

"Yeah, it's hot out here. I say we head back to the house, get more water, and figure it out."

The fifteen-minute walk to the house felt like hours. Making the last turn onto our street, I looked in every direction, holding onto the hope that Magic would come darting toward us.

"He's dead, I know it." Feeling helpless, tears rolled down my face. I looked over at Michael. I wasn't surprised that his face was wet, too. Dejected, we walked up our driveway and followed the winding sidewalk that led to the front door.

Approaching the last turn, unfamiliar shadows danced in the walkway ahead. I heard a familiar pant. When I ran to look, there was Magic! With a racing heart, I bolted to our doorstep.

"Oh my gosh, it's Magic!" I yelled. Magic, collapsed in an exhausted heap, was barely able to manage a muted yip. Saliva droplets fell to the concrete slab, disappearing as they hit the surface.

"Magic, Magic, where have you been?" Throwing my arms around his neck, I embraced him, kissing him all over the top of his head. "My sweet boy——oh my sweet boy. Ohhhhhh."

Michael and I stared at the hot mess in front of us.

Magic's lips looked like they had been painted with Marshmallow Fluff and his breathing was so shallow that his flanks fired like the pistons of an engine. I knelt beside him and then, like so many times before, I placed my hand at the nape of his neck. His buttery fur felt familiar, soothing. He had returned safely. He had come home.

"Oh my gosh, our sweet boy is back. Can you believe it?"

"Unbelievable." Michael beamed, as he reached down to float his hand over Magic's ears.

"Magic, you're a good boy to come home," Michael crooned. He gave me a loving look. "He's quite the dog, isn't he?"

"Oh, he is, he is," I answered happily. "Would you grab a towel from the garage and bring some fresh water for him? I'm not leaving him alone for one second."

"Sure," Michael said, running his hand over Magic's flank. "While I do that, why don't you check him for injuries?"

"Good idea."

As I skimmed my hand over his ear, Magic raised his head to nose my fingertips. "Magic, Magic," I said, scooping my arms around his neck and pulling him to my chest. "I love you so much." I buried my face into his neck until I heard the click of the front door.

I gently lowered Magic's head back onto the concrete. "I'm still in shock that Magic's here."

"Yeah, me too." Michael sighed. "Let's see if we can get him to drink some water. He's really hot."

"Let's wipe off his muzzle. Maybe that will get him interested in a drink."

Michael dipped the end of the towel in water, rung it out and gently swabbed the fluff from Magic's lips. We watched his dry tongue make wide sweeps across his chops.

"C'mon, sweet boy," I whispered. "Time to drink some water."

Magic started to roll onto his feet and then crashed to the concrete.

I looked over at Michael. "I think Magic is having a problem standing up." I reached out and picked up one of his paws. "Let's take a look at those feet." Every pad was red and swollen. "I think we need to wash his paws and get some antibiotic cream on them. They're going to take some time to heal."

Magic gingerly stood, teetering on all fours. He lapped up water and then dropped down and rolled over on his side again.

"Michael," I said hesitantly, searching his eyes for reassurance that he'd listen to what I was about to tell him. "I haven't said this before because it's an emotionally charged topic I didn't want to talk to anyone about. I adopted Magic because I thought he needed me, but I needed him, too. If only the adoption had been simpler. But it wasn't. His unpredictable behavior and emotional instability have kept us on a rollercoaster wondering if the ride will ever end. I worried whether I was capable of keeping him out of harm's way." I reached out and put my hand on Michael's arm. "That's when I contacted SAR." I peered down at Magic and stroked his ear. "What I wasn't counting on was what happened yesterday when he disappeared. Magic being gone only one night left me barely able to function. Can you imagine if we never saw him again? I'm not sure I'd ever get over it." I tightened my grip on Michael's arm.

Michael's denim blue eyes softened. "Lauren, I've known all along why you adopted Magic. It's true, I wasn't excited about the thought of taking in a rescue, but after Magic lived with us for two days, it was obvious you had a new-found purpose in helping him. One of your best qualities is that you have limitless determination. And that's good because you needed large amounts of that to be able to help him erase his past." Michael smiled warmly. "I supported you because I knew you loved him, unconditionally."

"Thanks for saying that, but what about you? Do you want to keep Magic?"

"You already know the answer to that question. I love him just as much as you do. And you've got to know that's how the kids feel, too."

I reached over and hugged Michael. "I love you and the kids so much."

Magic picked up his head. *"Hey, what about me?"*

"Did you hear that? That's the first time he's barked since we found him. That's a good sign, right?"

"Yes, it is. I think our boy is going to be okay."

Michael paused. "Do you think we should have him checked out at the vet?"

"I'm not sure any of us are up for that right now. Let's see how he does today."

"Okay, but let's get him out of the heat and into the house where we can keep an eye on him. And we need to text the kids and tell them the great news. They'll be so relieved!"

"They'll not only be relieved, they'll be ecstatic!"

Michael and I helped Magic to his feet. His steps were measured as he limped through the doorway.

"Magic, you're probably starving."

"Starving."

While I washed his paws and applied salve, Michael filled his food dish. As soon as Magic heard the kibble dancing inside the bowl, he stood and assisted Michael by nosing him until he put the dish on the floor. Magic inhaled the food in thirty seconds. I looked over at Michael and smiled. "Yup, other than a couple sore paws, I think he's going to be fine."

"I think you're right," Michael said cheerfully.

Exhausted from the emotional homecoming, I slumped onto the couch. Magic hobbled over and sat in front of me. He looked up at me expectantly and then threw both paws on my lap. His face was so close to mine that I felt the warm air from his nose. Stroking his ears, I thought about him as a hero. I knew he had earned the status of a search and rescue dog because he rescued Morgan and, in a different way, rescued me, too. Helping two human beings in his lifetime granted him that distinguished status forever.

The bond we shared was about unconditional love, the acceptance of each other's character flaws and the life lessons we experienced together, whether good or bad. If I had been able to get out of my head and listen to my heart, I would have known all along that Magic just wanted to be loved and cared for by our devoted family. I failed to see that what Magic needed most was my willingness to go above and beyond to protect and love him. That had always been enough. He had come back to me, showing me in only the way he knew how that all he needed could be found in his own back yard, with me. Like the first time we saw each other at the kennel, he looked back at me like I was the only person in the world.

"Love you, Mom."

The End

ACKNOWLEDGMENTS

As my teacher, Laurie says, if writing a book was easy, everyone would do it. Here are the people who inspired me along the way. Wes Stamm, who unleashed his adorable Labrador puppy in the Viking Range showroom, sparking my interest in dog ownership. The other dog lovers to thank are Desert Labrador Retriever Rescue (DLRR) who introduced me to the world of dog rescue. I will be forever grateful to Ann Phillips, shelter walker for DLRR, who saw Magic's potential at Maricopa County Animal Care and Control and transferred him into our organization. I was fortunate to have Dr. Mark Goldstein, a veterinarian and humane society advocate, spend countless hours counselling me about the intricacies of shelter organizations. Erin Chien-Szegedy, Marketing Director, for High County Humane Society, shared her wealth of facility experiences.

I owe gratitude to editors Barbara Youngs and Stephanie Gollobin for their expertise in reviewing the manuscript. First readers Bev Ahrensdorf, Lana Brozik, and Ann Rusher made valuable contributions to the story content. I want to thank Claudia Johnstone, a talented photographer, for her patience in capturing Magic's personality for the book cover. Photographer Del Colvin, snapped many fun-loving pictures of both dogs. I would be remiss if I didn't mention my easy-going and mentoring cover designer, Laura Duffy, who worked with me, through many edits. Shontelle Vidinghoff's graphic design input was invaluable as well. Amazing illustrator, Alison Lingley, further inspired me through her artistic genius. Her friendship from across the pond in Ireland was an unexpected highlight of writing the book. Rob Goluba tirelessly advised me and answered my questions about the world of self-publishing. I know it wasn't an easy task, so kudos to him for returning my phone calls.

I will be eternally grateful for all my friends who continued to cheer me on through the many stages of the writing process, with special thanks to Mary Matthews for editing the recipes.

Finally, I am indebted to my husband Rob, and our two kids, Taylor and Chad, who continually encouraged me to keep going and offered opinions and loving support along the way. With all my heart-felt thanks.

Amy Ahrensdorf

BAKED ZITI

Recipe By: Chef Amy Serving Size: 12 Preparation Time: 0:50

Ingredients:

1 lb. ziti pasta or any large macaroni

1 lb. ground beef or spicy ground turkey sausage

2 -28 oz jars of marinara sauce or pasta sauce

½ cup purchased or homemade pesto sauce

1 cup ricotta cheese

2 cups mozzarella cheese – shredded

½ cup parmesan cheese – grated, plus extra to garnish for the top

¼ cup mozzarella cheese -- shredded

Directions:

Preheat oven to 375 degrees. Prepare a 13 X 9 baking dish by coating with cooking spray.

Cook pasta according to package directions; drain, place in large bowl. Add pesto, ricotta, Parmesan and mozzarella cheese to the pasta. Mix well. Season with salt and pepper.

Sauté meat in a large skillet on medium heat until browned. Stir in jarred sauce to release brown bits on bottom of pan.

To assemble: Ladle 1/3 cup of the meat sauce on bottom of dish. Spoon 1/2 of the pasta mixture in the dish. Ladle another 1/3 of the sauce, then the remaining pasta. Top with the rest of the sauce. Sprinkle 1/4 cup mozzarella cheese over the top and remaining Parmesan cheese.

Coat foil with cooking spray. Cover and bake for 40 minutes or until bubbly. Uncover and bake 10 minutes. Let stand for 15 minutes before serving.

Note: Ziti can be frozen. Transfer from the freezer to the refrigerator the evening to defrost before baking.

CHOCOLATE TOFFEE SCONES

Recipe By: Chef Amy Serving Size: 6 Preparation Time: 0:30

Ingredients:
Dry mix:
3 ¼ cups sifted flour
½ cup granulated sugar
1 T baking powder
1 tsp baking soda
¼ tsp salt
1 cup chocolate chips
½ cup toasted pecan – chopped
½ cup toffee bits (such as Heath bars) – chopped
Wet mix:
2 cups chilled heavy cream -- whipped to stiff peaks
Pre-baking ingredients:
2 T butter – melted
2 T granulated sugar

Directions:
Preheat oven to 375. Cover 2 half-sheet baking pans with parchment. Sift flour and measure out 3 1/4 cups. Combine dry ingredients: flour, sugar, baking powder, baking soda, and salt in large bowl.

Stir chocolate chips, toasted, chopped nuts and toffee bits into the dry mixture.

Beat cream to stiff peaks and fold the whipped cream into dry ingredients. Mixture will be sticky.

Turn dough out onto lightly floured surface and gently knead dough for 1 minute. Pat into large disc.

Cut into 12 wedges with bench knife or cookie cutters.

Transfer to baking sheet 1 " apart, brush with butter then sprinkle with sugar.

Bake 12 - 14 minutes or until browned and dry to the touch.

EASY OATMEAL BLUEBERRY MUFFINS

Recipe By: Chef Amy Serving Size: 12 Preparation Time: 0:20

Ingredients:
Dry mix:
1 cup all-purpose flour

1 tsp baking powder

½ tsp baking soda

½ tsp salt

1 cup blueberries – fresh or frozen

Wet mix:
1 large egg

¼ cup butter – melted

¾ cup brown sugar

1 cup buttermilk

1 cup rolled oats

Directions:
Preheat oven to 400 degrees. Coat a 12-cup muffin tin with cooking spray.

In a small bowl, combine buttermilk and oats. Let mixture soak for 10 minutes. Melt butter in small bowl and set aside to cool.

In a large bowl, mix all of the dry ingredients.

In a medium bowl whisk egg with a fork until light in color. Add melted butter, brown sugar, and oats.

Gently fold wet ingredients into dry ingredients until just combined. DO NOT OVER MIX! Fold in blueberries.

Bake for 18 - 20 minutes.

Note: This recipe can be doubled or tripled. They freeze well.

HOGSBREATH DRY RUB

Recipe By: Richard McPeake Yield: 3 cups Preparation Time: 0:15

Ingredients:
  1 cup superfine sugar
  ½ cup kosher salt
  1 T granulated garlic
  2 T granulated onion
  2 T paprika
  ¼ cup chili powder
  2 tsp cumin powder
  1 T oregano
  2 tsp allspice – ground

Directions:
  Combine all ingredients in a medium size bowl. Stir, mixing well. Store in an air-tight container.

ASIAN FRUIT SALSA

Recipe By: Hugh Carpenter Serving Size: 4 Preparation Time: 0:35

Ingredients:
   2 mangos or 1 medium papaya – ½" cubes
   1 avocado – ½" cubed
   1 red bell pepper – small dice
   3 T cilantro – chopped
   2 green onion – minced
   Salsa dressing:
   2 T fresh ginger – finely minced
   2 T fresh orange juice
   2 T fresh lime juice
   2 T light brown sugar
   1 tsp sambal Oelek (or another chili paste)
   salt and pepper

Directions:
   For the salsa dressing: In a large bowl, combine minced ginger, fresh juices, brown sugar and chili sauce. Whisk until well combined. Refrigerate.

   In a large bowl, combine mangos or papaya, avocado, bell pepper, cilantro and green onion. Refrigerate.

   When ready to serve, combine fruit with the salsa dressing. Stir gently. Season with salt and pepper.

MEDJOOL DATES WITH MASCARPONE AND PISTACHIOS

Recipe By: Chef Amy Serving Size: 4 Preparation Time: 0:15

Ingredients:

12 medjool dates – pitted
2 oz pistachios – finely chopped
6 T mascarpone cheese

Directions:

Using a small knife, slit the date lengthwise. Slice downward until reaching the pit. Open the date with your fingers and pull out the pit.

Using a spoon, fill the center with the mascarpone cheese. Roll the surface in finely chopped pistachios.

Note: The dates can be served as an appetizer or desert. Assemble ahead and store in the refrigerator.

JALAPENO BACON

Recipe By: Chef Amy Serving Size: 6 Preparation Time: 0:15

Ingredients:

   1 lb. regular sliced bacon, not thick cut
   jalapeno powder -- to taste
   ¼ cup light brown sugar
   ½ cup raw pecans – chopped fine
   2 sheets of parchment paper

Directions:

   Preheat oven to 375 degrees on convection setting. If using a bake setting, rotate the pans after 10 minutes.

   Line two half sheet baking pans with parchment paper.

   Place bacon strips on a sheet pan. Do not overlap.

   Dust the surface with jalapeno powder. Sprinkle the brown sugar evenly over the strips. Smooth out any lumps using the back of a spoon. Uniformly sprinkle the chopped pecans over the sugar coating.

   Bake until bacon is cooked through and is browned and crispy - about 20 minutes. Do not turn the bacon slices over. Drain on a paper towel.